MW00668563

Guidelines for Assessment and Instruction in Statistics Education (GAISE) Report

A PRE-K-12 CURRICULUM FRAMEWORK

CHRISTINE FRANKLIN
University of Georgia

GARY KADER
Appalachian State University

DENISE MEWBORN
University of Georgia

JERRY MORENO
John Carroll University

ROXY PECK
California Polytechnic State University, San Luis Obispo

MIKE PERRY
Appalachian State University

RICHARD SCHEAFFER
University of Florida

Endorsed by the American Statistical Association
August 2005

Library of Congress Cataloging-in-Publication Data
Guidelines for assessment and instruction in statistics education
(GAISE) report: a pre-k–12 curriculum framework / Authors, Christine
Franklin ... [et al.].

    p. cm.
  Includes bibliographical references.
  ISBN-13: 978-0-9791747-1-1 (pbk.)
  ISBN-10: 0-9791747-1-6 (pbk.)
1. Statistics–Study and teaching (Early childhood)–Standards.
2. Statistics–Study and teaching (Elementary)–Standards.
3. Statistics–Study and teaching (Secondary)–Standards
I. Franklin, Christine A

QA276.18.G85 2007
519.5071–dc22

                                      2006103096

© 2007 by American Statistical Association
Alexandria, VA 22314

Also available online at *www.amstat.org/education/gaise*. All rights reserved.
No part of this book may be reproduced, in any form or by any means,
without permission in writing from the publisher.

Printed in the United States of America
10 9 8 7 6 5 4 3 2 1

978-0-9791747-1-1
0-9791747-1-6

Advisors

Susan Friel
The University of North Carolina

Landy Godbold
Westminster Schools

Brad Hartlaub
Kenyon College

Peter Holmes
Nottingham Trent University

Cliff Konold
University of Massachusetts/Amherst

Production Team

Christine Franklin
University of Georgia

Nicholas Horton
Smith College

Gary Kader
Appalachian State University

Jerry Moreno
John Carroll University

Megan Murphy
American Statistical Association

Valerie Snider
American Statistical Association

Daren Starnes
Fountain Valley School of Colorado

Special Thanks

The authors extend a special thank you
to the American Statistical Association
Board of Directors for funding the
writing process of GAISE as a strategic
initiative and to the ASA/NCTM Joint
Committee for funding the production
of the GAISE Framework.

Cover photo by Andres Rodriguez
Book design by Valerie Snider

Contents

Introduction   1

Framework   11

The Role of Variability in the Problem-Solving Process   11

Maturing over Levels   12

The *Framework* Model   13

Illustrations   16

Detailed Descriptions of Each Level   21

Level A   23

Example 1: Choosing the Band for the End of the Year Party—Conducting a Survey   24

Comparing Groups   27

The Simple Experiment   28

Example 2: Growing Beans—A Simple Comparative Experiment   28

Making Use of Available Data   29

Describing Center and Spread   29

Looking for an Association   31

Example 3: Purchasing Sweat Suits—The Role of Height and Arm Span   31

Understanding Variability   33

The Role of Probability   33

Misuses of Statistics   35

Summary of Level A   35

Level B   37

Example 1, Level A Revisited: Choosing a Band for the School Dance   38

Connecting Two Categorical Variables   40

Questionnaires and Their Difficulties   41

Measure of Location—The Mean as a Balance Point   41

A Measure of Spread—The Mean Absolute Deviation   44

Representing Data Distributions—The Frequency Table and Histogram   44

Comparing Distributions—The Boxplot   46

Measuring the Strength of Association between Two Quantitative Variables   48

Modeling Linear Association   51

The Importance of Random Selection   52

Comparative Experiments   54

Time Series   55

Misuses of Statistics   56

Summary of Level B   58

Level C   61

An Introductory Example—Obesity in America   62

The Investigatory Process at Level C   64

Example 1: The Sampling Distribution of a Sample Proportion   67

Example 2: The Sampling Distribution of a Sample Mean   69

Example 3: A Survey of Music Preferences   71

Example 4: An Experiment on the Effects of Light on the Growth of Radish Seedlings   75

Example 5: Estimating the Density of the Earth—A Classical Study   79

Example 6: Linear Regression Analysis—Height vs. Forearm Length   80

Example 7: Comparing Mathematics Scores—An Observational Study   82

Example 8: Observational Study—Toward Establishing Causation   83

The Role of Probability in Statistics   84

Summary of Level C   87

Appendix for Level A   89

Appendix for Level B   95

Appendix for Level C   99

References   108

Index of Tables and Figures

Table 1: The Framework 14–15

Table 2: Frequency Count Table 24

Table 3: Frequencies and Relative Frequencies 39

Table 4: Two-Way Frequency Table 40, 95

Table 5: Grouped Frequency and Grouped Relative Frequency Distributions 46

Table 6: Hat Size Data 47

Table 7: Five-Number Summaries for Sodium Content 47

Table 8: Height and Arm Span Data 48

Table 9: Five-Number Summaries 55

Table 10: Live Birth Data 56

Table 11: Two-Way Frequency Table 72

Table 12: Lengths of Radish Seedlings 76

Table 13: Treatment Summary Statistics 77

Table 14: Heights vs. Forearm Lengths 81, 99

Table 15: NAEP 2000 Scores in Mathematics 82

Table 16: Cigarette Smoking and Lung Cancer 83

Table 17: Level of Cigarette Smoking and Lung Cancer 84

Table 18: Family Size Distribution 86

Table 19: 2x2 Two-Way Frequency Table 96

Table 20: Two-Way Frequency Table 97

Table 21: Two-Way Frequency Table 97

Table 22: Two-Way Frequency Table 98

Table 23: Result of Lifestyle Question 100

Table 24: Pulse Data 102

Table 25: Pulse Data in Matched Pairs 102

Table 26: U.S. Population (in 1,000s) 104

Table 27: U.S. Death Rates (Deaths per 100,000 of Population) 105

Table 28: Enrollment Data 106

Figure 1: Picture Graph of Music Preferences 25

Figure 2: Bar Graph of Music Preferences 26

Figure 3: Stem and Leaf Plot of Jumping Distances 27

Figure 4: Dotplot of Environment vs. Height 28

Figure 5: Parallel Dotplot of Sodium Content 29

Figure 6: Scatterplot of Arm Span vs. Height 32

Figure 7: Timeplot of Temperature vs. Time 32

Figure 8: Comparative Bar Graph for Music Preferences 39

Figure 9: Dotplot for Pet Count 42

Figure 10: Dotplot Showing Pets Evenly Distributed 42

Figure 11: Dotplot with One Data Point Moved 42

Figure 12: Dotplot with Two Data Points Moved 42

Figure 13: Dotplot with Different Data Points Moved 43

Figure 14: Dotplot Showing Distance from 5 43

Figure 15: Dotplot Showing Original Data and Distance from 5 43

Figure 16: Stemplot of Head Circumference 45

Figure 17: Relative Frequency Histogram 45

Figure 18: Boxplot for Sodium Content 47

Figure 19: Scatterplot of Arm Span vs. Height 49

Figure 20: Scatterplot Showing Means 49

Figure 21: Eyeball Line 51

Figure 22: Eighty Circles 53

Figure 23: Boxplot for Memory Data 55

Figure 24: Time Series Plot of Live Births 56

Figure 25: Histogram of Sample Proportions 68

Figure 26: Histogram of Sample Means 69

Figure 27: Dotplot of Sample Proportions from a Hypothetical Population in Which 50% Like Rap Music 72

Figure 28: Dotplot of Sample Proportions from a Hypothetical Population in Which 40% Like Rap Music 73

Figure 29: Dotplot Showing Simulated Sampling Distribution 74

Figure 30: Seed Experiment 75

Figure 31: Boxplot Showing Growth under Different Conditions 77

Figure 32: Dotplot Showing Differences of Means 78

Figure 33: Dotplot Showing Differences of Means 78

Figure 34: Histogram of Earth Density Measurements 80

Figure 35: Scatterplot and Residual Plot 81, 99

Figure 36: Random Placement of Names 89

Figure 37: Names Clustered by Length 90

Figure 38: Preliminary Dotplot 90

Figure 39: Computer-Generated Dotplot 91

Figure 40: Student-Drawn Graphs 92

Figure 41: Initial Sorting of Candies 93

Figure 42: Bar Graph of Candy Color 93

Figure 43: Scatterplot of Arm Span/Height Data 95

Figure 44: Dotplot Showing Association 100

Figure 45: Dotplot Showing Differences in Sample Proportions 101

Figure 46: Dotplot of Randomized Differences in Means 103

Figure 47: Dotplot of Randomized Pair Difference Means 104

Figure 48: Scatterplot of Death Rates 105

Figure 49: Scatterplot of Actual Deaths 105

Figure 50: Distorted Graph 106

Figure 51: Plot of African-American vs. Total Enrollments 107

Figure 52: Plot of African-American Enrollments Only 107

Figure 53: Ratio of African-American to Total Enrollments 107

Introduction

The ultimate goal: statistical literacy. Every morning, the newspaper and other media confront us with statistical information on topics ranging from the economy to education, from movies to sports, from food to medicine, and from public opinion to social behavior. Such information guides decisions in our personal lives and enables us to meet our responsibilities as citizens. At work, we may be presented with quantitative information on budgets, supplies, manufacturing specifications, market demands, sales forecasts, or workloads. Teachers may be confronted with educational statistics concerning student performance or their own accountability. Medical scientists must understand the statistical results of experiments used for testing the effectiveness and safety of drugs. Law enforcement professionals depend on crime statistics. If we consider changing jobs and moving to another community, then our decision can be affected by statistics about cost of living, crime rate, and educational quality.

Our lives are governed by numbers. Every high-school graduate should be able to use sound statistical reasoning to intelligently cope with the requirements of citizenship, employment, and family and to be prepared for a healthy, happy, and productive life.

Citizenship

Public opinion polls are the most visible examples of a statistical application that has an impact on our lives.

In addition to directly informing individual citizens, polls are used by others in ways that affect us. The political process employs opinion polls in several ways. Candidates for office use polling to guide campaign strategy. A poll can determine a candidate's strengths with voters, which can, in turn, be emphasized in the campaign. Citizens also might be suspicious that poll results might influence candidates to take positions just because they are popular.

A citizen informed by polls needs to understand that the results were determined from a sample of the population under study, that the reliability of the results depends on how the sample was selected, and that the results are subject to sampling error. The statistically literate citizen should understand the behavior of "random" samples and be able to interpret a "margin of sampling error."

The federal government has been in the statistics business from its very inception. The U.S. Census was established in 1790 to provide an official count of the population for the purpose of allocating representatives to Congress. Not only has the role of the U.S. Census Bureau greatly expanded to include the collection of a broad spectrum of socioeconomic data, but other federal departments also produce extensive "official" statistics concerned with agriculture, health, education, environment, and commerce. The information gathered by these agencies influences policy making and helps to determine priorities for

> " Every high-school graduate should be able to use sound statistical reasoning to intelligently cope with the requirements of citizenship, employment, and family and to be prepared for a healthy, happy, and productive life. "

government spending. It is also available for general use by individuals or private groups. Thus, statistics compiled by government agencies have a tremendous impact on the life of the ordinary citizen.

Personal Choices

Statistical literacy is required for daily personal choices. Statistics provides information about the nutritional quality of foods and thus informs our choices at the grocery store. Statistics helps to establish the safety and effectiveness of drugs, which aids physicians in prescribing a treatment. Statistics also helps to establish the safety of toys to assure our children are not at risk. Our investment choices are guided by a plethora of statistical information about stocks and bonds. The Nielsen ratings help determine which shows will survive on television, thus affecting what is available. Many products have a statistical history, and our choices of products can be affected by awareness of this history. The design of an automobile is aided by anthropometrics—the statistics of the human body—to enhance passenger comfort. Statistical ratings of fuel efficiency, safety, and reliability are available to help us select a vehicle.

The Workplace and Professions

Individuals who are prepared to use statistical thinking in their careers will have the opportunity to advance to more rewarding and challenging positions.

A statistically competent work force will allow the United States to compete more effectively in the global marketplace and to improve its position in the international economy. An investment in statistical literacy is an investment in our nation's economic future, as well as in the well-being of individuals.

The competitive marketplace demands quality. Efforts to improve quality and accountability are prominent among the many ways that statistical thinking and tools can be used to enhance productivity. Quality-control practices, such as the statistical monitoring of design and manufacturing processes, identify where improvement can be made and lead to better product quality. Systems of accountability can help produce more effective employees and organizations, but many accountability systems now in place are not based on sound statistical principles and may, in fact, have the opposite effect. Good accountability systems require proper use of statistical tools to determine and apply appropriate criteria.

Science

Life expectancy in the US almost doubled during the 20th century; this rapid increase in life span is the consequence of science. Science has enabled us to improve medical care and procedures, food production, and the detection and prevention of epidemics. Statistics plays a prominent role in this scientific progress.

The U.S. Food and Drug Administration requires extensive testing of drugs to determine effectiveness and side effects before they can be sold. A recent advertisement for a drug designed to reduce blood clots stated, "PLAVIX, added to aspirin and your current medications, helps raise your protection against heart attack or stroke." But the advertisement also warned, "The risk of bleeding may increase with PLAVIX..."

Statistical literacy involves a healthy dose of skepticism about "scientific" findings. Is the information about side effects of PLAVIX treatment reliable? A statistically literate person should ask such questions and be able to intelligently answer them. A statistically literate high-school graduate will be able to understand the conclusions from scientific investigations and offer an informed opinion about the legitimacy of the reported results. According to *Mathematics and Democracy: The Case for Quantitative Literacy* (Steen, 2001), such knowledge "empowers people by giving them tools to think for themselves, to ask intelligent questions of experts, and to confront authority confidently. These are skills required to survive in the modern world."

Statistical literacy is essential in our personal lives as consumers, citizens, and professionals. Statistics plays a role in our health and happiness. Sound statistical reasoning skills take a long time to develop. They cannot be honed to the level needed in the modern world through one high-school course. The surest way to help students attain the necessary skill level is to begin the statistics education process in the elementary grades and keep strengthening and expanding students' statistical thinking skills throughout the middle- and high-school years. A statistically literate high-school graduate will know how to interpret the data in the morning newspaper and will ask the right questions about statistical claims. He or she will be comfortable handling quantitative decisions that come up on the job, and will be able to make informed decisions about quality-of-life issues.

The remainder of this document lays out a curriculum framework for pre-K–12 educational programs that is designed to help students achieve statistical literacy.

The Case for Statistics Education

Over the past quarter century, statistics (often labeled data analysis and probability) has become a key component of the pre-K–12 mathematics curriculum. Advances in technology and modern methods of data analysis in the 1980s, coupled with the data richness of society in the information age, led to the development of curriculum materials geared toward introducing statistical concepts into the school curriculum as early as the elementary grades. This grassroots effort was given sanction by the National Council of Teachers of Mathematics (NCTM) when their influential document, *Curriculum and Evaluation Standards for School Mathematics* (NCTM, 1989), included "Data Analysis

" Statistics
education as
proposed
in this
Framework can
promote the
'must-have'
competencies
for graduates
to 'thrive in the
modern world.' "

and Probability" as one of the five content strands. As this document and its 2000 replacement, *Principles and Standards for School Mathematics* (NCTM, 2000), became the basis for reform of mathematics curricula in many states, the acceptance of and interest in statistics as part of mathematics education gained strength. In recent years, many mathematics educators and statisticians have devoted large segments of their careers to improving statistics education materials and pedagogical techniques.

NCTM is not the only group calling for improved statistics education beginning at the school level. The National Assessment of Educational Progress (NAEP, 2005) was developed around the same content strands as the NCTM *Standards*, with data analysis and probability questions playing an increasingly prominent role on the NAEP exam. In 2006, the College Board released its *College Board Standards for College Success™: Mathematics and Statistics*, which includes "Data and Variation" and "Chance, Fairness, and Risk" among its list of eight topic areas that are "central to the knowledge and skills developed in the middle-school and high-school years." An examination of the standards recommended by this document reveals a consistent emphasis on data analysis, probability, and statistics at each course level.

The emerging quantitative literacy movement calls for greater emphasis on practical quantitative skills that will help assure success for high-school graduates in life and work; many of these skills are statistical in nature. To quote from *Mathematics and Democracy: The Case for Quantitative Literacy* (Steen, 2001):

> Quantitative literacy, also called numeracy, is the natural tool for comprehending information in the computer age. The expectation that ordinary citizens be quantitatively literate is primarily a phenomenon of the late twentieth century. ...Unfortunately, despite years of study and life experience in an environment immersed in data, many educated adults remain functionally illiterate. ...Quantitative literacy empowers people by giving them tools to think for themselves [sic], to ask intelligent questions of experts, and to confront authority confidently. These are the skills required to thrive in the modern world.

A recent study from the American Diploma Project, titled *Ready or Not: Creating a High School Diploma That Counts* (*www.amstat.org/education/gaise/1*), recommends "must-have" competencies needed for high-school graduates "to succeed in postsecondary education or in high-performance, high-growth jobs." These include, in addition to algebra and geometry, aspects of data analysis, statistics, and other applications that are vitally important for other subjects, as well as for employment in today's data-rich economy.

Statistics education as proposed in this *Framework* can promote the "must-have" competencies for graduates to "thrive in the modern world."

NCTM Standards and the Framework

The main objective of this document is to provide a conceptual *Framework* for K–12 statistics education. The foundation for this *Framework* rests on the NCTM *Principles and Standards for School Mathematics* (2000).

The *Framework* is intended to complement the recommendations of the NCTM *Principles and Standards*, not to supplant them.

The NCTM *Principles and Standards* describes the statistics content strand as follows:

Data Analysis and Probability

Instructional programs from pre-kindergarten through grade 12 should enable all students to:

→ formulate questions that can be addressed with data and collect, organize, and display relevant data to answer them;

→ select and use appropriate statistical methods to analyze data;

→ develop and evaluate inferences and predictions that are based on data; and

→ understand and apply basic concepts of probability.

The "Data Analysis and Probability" standard recommends that students formulate questions that can be answered using data and address what is involved in wisely gathering and using that data. Students should learn how to collect data, organize their own or others' data, and display the data in graphs and charts that will be useful in answering their questions. This standard also includes learning methods for analyzing data and ways of making inferences and drawing conclusions from data. The basic concepts and applications of probability also are addressed, with an emphasis on the way probability and statistics are related.

The NCTM *Principles and Standards* elaborates on these themes somewhat and provides examples of the types of lessons and activities that might be used in a classroom. More complete examples can be found in the NCTM *Navigation Series on Data Analysis and Probability* (2002–2004). Statistics, however, is a relatively new subject for many teachers, who have not had an opportunity to develop sound knowledge of the principles and concepts underlying the practices of data analysis that they now are called upon to teach. These teachers do not clearly understand the difference between statistics and mathematics. They do not see the statistics curriculum for grades pre-K–12 as a cohesive and coherent curriculum strand. These teachers may not see how the overall statistics curriculum provides a developmental sequence of learning experiences.

This *Framework* provides a conceptual structure for statistics education that gives a coherent picture of the overall curriculum.

The Difference between Statistics and Mathematics

"Statistics is a methodological discipline. It exists not for itself, but rather to offer to other fields of study a coherent set of ideas and tools for dealing with data. The need for such a discipline arises from the *omnipresence of variability*." (Moore and Cobb, 1997)

A major objective of statistics education is to help students develop statistical thinking. Statistical thinking, in large part, must deal with this omnipresence of variability; statistical problem solving and decision making depend on understanding, explaining, and quantifying the variability in the data.

It is this focus on *variability in data* that sets apart statistics from mathematics.

The Nature of Variability

There are many sources of variability in data. Some of the important sources are described below.

Measurement Variability—Repeated measurements on the same individual vary. Sometimes two measurements vary because the measuring device produces unreliable results, such as when we try to measure a large distance with a small ruler. At other times, variability results from changes in the system being measured. For example, even with a precise measuring device, your recorded blood pressure could differ from one moment to the next.

Natural Variability—Variability is inherent in nature. Individuals are different. When we measure the same quantity across several individuals, we are bound to get differences in the measurements. Although some of this may be due to our measuring instrument, most of it is simply due to the fact that individuals differ. People naturally have different heights, different aptitudes and abilities, and different opinions and emotional responses. When we measure any one of these traits, we are bound to get variability in the measurements. Different seeds for the same variety of bean will grow to different sizes when subjected to the same environment because no two seeds are exactly alike; there is bound to be variability from seed to seed in the measurements of growth.

Induced Variability—If we plant one pack of bean seeds in one field, and another pack of seeds in another location with a different climate, then an observed difference in growth among the seeds in one location with those in the other might be due to inherent differences in the seeds (natural variability), or the observed difference might be due to the fact that the locations are not the same. If one type of fertilizer is used on one field and another type on the other, then observed differences might be due to the difference in fertilizers. For that matter, the observed difference might be due to a factor we haven't even thought about. A more carefully designed experiment can help us determine the effects of different factors.

This one basic idea, comparing natural variability to the variability induced by other factors, forms the heart of modern statistics. It has allowed medical science to conclude that some drugs are effective and safe, whereas others are ineffective or have harmful side effects. It has been employed by agricultural scientists to demonstrate that a variety of corn grows better in one climate than another, that one fertilizer is more effective than another, or that one type of feed is better for beef cattle than another.

Sampling Variability—In a political poll, it seems reasonable to use the proportion of voters surveyed (a sample statistic) as an estimate of the unknown proportion of all voters who support a particular candidate. But if a second sample of the same size is used, it is almost certain that there would not be exactly the same proportion of voters in the sample who support the candidate. The value of the sample proportion will vary from sample to sample. This is called sampling variability. So what is to keep one sample from estimating that the true proportion is .60 and another from saying it is .40? This is possible, but unlikely, if proper sampling techniques are used. Poll results are useful because these techniques and an adequate sample size can ensure that unacceptable differences among samples are quite unlikely.

An excellent discussion on the nature of variability is given in *Seeing Through Statistics* (Utts, 1999).

The Role of Context

"The focus on variability naturally gives statistics a particular content that sets it apart from mathematics, itself, and from other mathematical sciences, but there is more than just content that distinguishes statistical thinking from mathematics. Statistics requires a different kind of thinking, because *data are not just numbers, they are numbers with a context*. In mathematics, context obscures structure. In data analysis, context provides meaning." (Moore and Cobb, 1997)

Many mathematics problems arise from applied contexts, but the context is removed to reveal mathematical patterns. Statisticians, like mathematicians, look for patterns, but the meaning of the patterns depends on the context.

A graph that occasionally appears in the business section of newspapers shows a plot of the Dow Jones Industrial Average (DJIA) over a 10-year period. The variability of stock prices draws the attention of an investor. This stock index may go up or down over intervals of time, and may fall or rise sharply over a short period. In context, the graph raises questions. A serious investor is not only interested in when or how rapidly the index goes up or down, but also why. What was going on in the world when the market went up; what was going on when it went down? Now strip away the context. Remove time (years) from the horizontal axis and call it "X," remove stock value (DJIA)

> " In mathematics, context obscures structure. In data analysis, context provides meaning. "

from the vertical axis and call it "Y," and there remains a graph of very little interest or mathematical content!

Probability

Probability is a tool for statistics.

Probability is an important part of any mathematical education. It is a part of mathematics that enriches the subject as a whole by its interactions with other uses of mathematics. Probability is an essential tool in applied mathematics and mathematical modeling. It is also an essential tool in statistics.

The use of probability as a mathematical model and the use of probability as a tool in statistics employ not only different approaches, but also different kinds of reasoning. Two problems and the nature of the solutions will illustrate the difference.

Problem 1:

Assume a coin is "fair."

Question: If we toss the coin five times, how many heads will we get?

Problem 2:

You pick up a coin.

Question: Is this a fair coin?

Problem 1 is a mathematical probability problem. Problem 2 is a statistics problem that can use the mathematical probability model determined in Problem 1 as a tool to seek a solution.

The answer to neither question is deterministic. Coin tossing produces random outcomes, which suggests that the answer is probabilistic. The solution to Problem 1 starts with the assumption that the coin is fair and proceeds to logically *deduce* the numerical probabilities for each possible number of heads: 0, 1,..., 5.

The solution to Problem 2 starts with an unfamiliar coin; we don't know if it is fair or biased. The search for an answer is experimental—toss the coin and see what happens. Examine the resulting data to see if it looks as if it came from a fair coin or a biased coin. There are several possible approaches, including toss the coin five times and record the number of heads. Then, do it again: Toss the coin five times and record the number of heads. Repeat 100 times. Compile the frequencies of outcomes for each possible number of heads. Compare these results to the frequencies predicted by the mathematical model for a fair coin in Problem 1. If the empirical frequencies from the experiment are quite dissimilar from those predicted by the mathematical model for a fair coin and are not likely to be caused by random variation in coin tosses, then we conclude that the coin is not fair. In this case, we *induce* an answer by making a general conclusion from observations of experimental results.

Probability and Chance Variability

Two important uses of "randomization" in statistical work occur in sampling and experimental design. When sampling, we "select at random," and in experiments, we randomly assign individuals to different treatments. Randomization does much more than remove bias in selections and assignments. Randomization leads to *chance variability* in outcomes that can be described with probability models.

The probability of something says about what percent of the time it is expected to happen when the basic process is repeated over and over again. Probability theory does not say very much about one toss of a coin; it makes predictions about the long-run behavior of many coin tosses.

Probability tells us little about the consequences of random selection for one sample, but describes the variation we expect to see in samples when the sampling process is repeated a large number of times. Probability tells us little about the consequences of random assignment for one experiment, but describes the variation we expect to see in the results when the experiment is replicated a large number of times.

When randomness is present, the statistician wants to know if the observed result is due to chance or something else. This is the idea of *statistical significance*.

The Role of Mathematics in Statistics Education

The evidence that statistics is different from mathematics is not presented to argue that mathematics is not important to statistics education or that statistics education should not be a part of mathematics education. To the contrary, statistics education becomes increasingly mathematical as the level of understanding goes up. But data collection design, exploration of data, and the interpretation of results should be emphasized in statistics education for statistical literacy. These are heavily dependent on context, and, at the introductory level, involve limited formal mathematics.

Probability plays an important role in statistical analysis, but formal mathematical probability should have its own place in the curriculum. Pre-college statistics education should emphasize the ways probability is used in statistical thinking; an intuitive grasp of probability will suffice at these levels.

In This Section

→ The Role of Variability in the Problem-Solving Process

→ Maturing over Levels

→ The *Framework* Model

→ Illustrations

   I. Formulate Questions

      Word Length Example

      Popular Music Example

      Height and Arm Span Example

      Plant Growth Example

   II. Collect Data

      Word Length Example

      Plant Growth Example

   III. Analyze Data

      Popular Music Example

      Height and Arm Span Example

   IV. Interpret Results

      Word Length Example

      Plant Growth Example

Nature of Variability

Variability within a Group

Variability within a Group and Variability between Groups

Covariability

Variability in Model Fitting

Induced Variability

Sampling Variability

Chance Variability from Sampling

Chance Variability Resulting from Assignment to Groups in Experiments

→ Detailed Descriptions of Each Level

Statistical problem solving is an investigative process that involves four components:

I. Formulate Questions

→ clarify the problem at hand

→ formulate one (or more) questions that can be answered with data

II. Collect Data

→ design a plan to collect appropriate data

→ employ the plan to collect the data

III. Analyze Data

→ select appropriate graphical and numerical methods

→ use these methods to analyze the data

IV. Interpret Results

→ interpret the analysis

→ relate the interpretation to the original question

The Role of Variability in the Problem-Solving Process

I. Formulate Questions

Anticipating Variability—Making the Statistics Question Distinction

The formulation of a statistics question requires an understanding of the difference between a question

that anticipates a deterministic answer and a question that anticipates an answer based on data that vary.

The question, "How tall am I?" will be answered with a single height. It is not a statistics question. The question "How tall are adult men in the USA?" would not be a statistics question if all these men were exactly the same height! The fact that there are differing heights, however, implies that we anticipate an answer based on measurements of height that vary. This is a statistics question.

The poser of the question, "How does sunlight affect the growth of a plant?" should anticipate that the growth of two plants of the same type exposed to the same sunlight will likely differ. This is a statistics question.

The anticipation of variability is the basis for understanding the statistics question distinction.

II. Collect Data

Acknowledging Variability—Designing for Differences

Data collection designs must acknowledge variability in data, and frequently are intended to reduce variability. Random sampling is intended to reduce the differences between sample and population. The sample size influences the effect of sampling variability (error). Experimental designs are chosen to acknowledge the differences between groups subjected to different treatments. Random assignment to the groups is intended to reduce differences between the groups due to factors that are not manipulated in the experiment.

> " The formulation of a statistics question requires an understanding of the difference between a question that anticipates a deterministic answer and a question that anticipates an answer based on data that vary. "

Some experimental designs pair subjects so they are similar. Twins frequently are paired in medical experiments so that observed differences might be more likely attributed to the difference in treatments, rather than differences in the subjects.

The understanding of data collection designs that acknowledge differences is required for effective collection of data.

III. Analyze Data

Accounting of Variability—Using Distributions

The main purpose of statistical analysis is to give an accounting of the variability in the data. When results of an election poll state "42% of those polled support a particular candidate with margin of error +/- 3% at the 95% confidence level," the focus is on sampling variability. The poll gives an estimate of the support among all voters. The margin of error indicates how far the sample result (42% +/- 3%) might differ from the actual percent of all voters who support the candidate. The confidence level tells us how often estimates produced by the method employed will produce correct results. This analysis is based on the distribution of estimates from repeated random sampling.

When test scores are described as "normally distributed with mean 450 and standard deviation 100," the focus is on how the scores differ from the mean. The normal distribution describes a bell-shaped pattern of scores, and the standard deviation indicates the level of variation of the scores from the mean.

Accounting for variability with the use of distributions is the key idea in the analysis of data.

IV. Interpret Results

Allowing for Variability—Looking beyond the Data

Statistical interpretations are made in the presence of variability and must allow for it.

The result of an election poll must be interpreted as an estimate that can vary from sample to sample. The generalization of the poll results to the entire population of voters looks beyond the sample of voters surveyed and must allow for the possibility of variability of results among different samples. The results of a randomized comparative medical experiment must be interpreted in the presence of variability due to the fact that different individuals respond differently to the same treatment and the variability due to randomization. The generalization of the results looks beyond the data collected from the subjects who participated in the experiment and must allow for these sources of variability.

Looking beyond the data to make generalizations must allow for variability in the data.

Maturing over Levels

The mature statistician understands the role of variability in the statistical problem-solving process. At the point of question formulation, the statistician anticipates the data collection, the nature of the analysis, and the possible interpretations—all of which involve possible sources of variability. In the end, the mature practitioner reflects upon all aspects of data collection and analysis as well as the question, itself, when interpreting results. Likewise, he or she links data collection and analysis to each other and the other two components.

Beginning students cannot be expected to make all of these linkages. They require years of experience and training. Statistical education should be viewed as a developmental process. To meet the proposed goals, this report provides a framework for statistical education over three levels. If the goal were to produce a mature practicing statistician, there certainly would be several levels beyond these. There is no attempt to tie these levels to specific grade levels.

The *Framework* uses three developmental Levels: A, B, and C. Although these three levels may parallel grade levels, they are based on development in statistical literacy, not age. Thus, a middle-school student who has had no prior experience with statistics will need to begin with Level A concepts and activities before moving to Level B. This holds true for a secondary student as well. If a student hasn't had Level A and B experiences prior to high school, then it is not appropriate for that student to jump into Level C expectations. The learning is more teacher-driven at Level A, but becomes student-driven at Levels B and C.

The *Framework* Model

The conceptual structure for statistics education is provided in the two-dimensional model shown in Table 1. One dimension is defined by the problem-solving process components plus the nature of the variability considered and how we focus on variability. The second dimension is comprised of the three developmental levels.

Each of the first four rows describes a process component as it develops across levels. The fifth row indicates the nature of the variability considered at a given level. It is understood that work at Level B assumes and develops further the concepts from Level A; likewise, Level C assumes and uses concepts from the lower levels.

Reading down a column will describe a complete problem investigation for a particular level along with the nature of the variability considered.

Table 1: The Framework

Process Component	Level A	Level B	Level C
I. Formulate Question	**Beginning awareness of the *statistics question distinction***	**Increased awareness of the *statistics question distinction***	**Students can make the *statistics question distinction***
	Teachers pose questions of interest	Students begin to pose their own questions of interest	Students pose their own questions of interest
	Questions restricted to the classroom	Questions not restricted to the classroom	Questions seek generalization
II. Collect Data	Do not yet *design for differences*	Beginning awareness of *design for differences*	Students make *design for differences*
	Census of classroom	Sample surveys; begin to use random selection	Sampling designs with random selection
	Simple experiment	Comparative experiment; begin to use random allocation	Experimental designs with randomization
III. Analyze Data	*Use* particular properties of *distributions* in the context of a specific example	Learn to *use* particular properties of *distributions* as tools of analysis	Understand and *use distributions* in analysis as a global concept
	Display variability within a group	Quantify variability within a group	Measure variability within a group; measure variability between groups
	Compare individual to individual	Compare group to group in displays	Compare group to group using displays and measures of variability
	Compare individual to group	Acknowledge sampling error	Describe and quantify sampling error
	Beginning awareness of group to group	Some quantification of association; simple models for association	Quantification of association; fitting of models for association
	Observe association between two variables		

14

Process Component	Level A	Level B	Level C
IV. Interpret Results	Students do not look *beyond the data* No generalization beyond the classroom Note difference between two individuals with different conditions Observe association in displays	Students acknowledge that *looking beyond the data* is feasible Acknowledge that a sample may or may not be representative of the larger population Note the difference between two groups with different conditions Aware of distinction between observational study and experiment Note differences in strength of association Basic interepretation of models for association Aware of the distinction between association and cause and effect	Students are able to *look beyond the data* in some contexts Generalize from sample to population Aware of the effect of randomization on the results of experiments Understand the difference between observational studies and experiments Interpret measures of strength of association Interpret models of association Distinguish between conclusions from association studies and experiments
Nature of Variability	Measurement variability Natural variability Induced variability	Sampling variability	Chance variability
Focus on Variability	Variability within a group	Variability within a group and variability between groups Covariability	Variability in model fitting

"The illustrations of learning activities given here are intended to clarify the differences across the developmental levels for each component of the problem-solving process."

Illustrations

All four steps of the problem-solving process are used at all three levels, but the depth of understanding and sophistication of methods used increases across Levels A, B, and C. This maturation in understanding the problem-solving process and its underlying concepts is paralleled by an increasing complexity in the role of variability. The illustrations of learning activities given here are intended to clarify the differences across the developmental levels for each component of the problem-solving process. Later sections will give illustrations of the complete problem-solving process for learning activities at each level.

I. Formulate Questions

Word Length Example

Level A: How long are the words on this page?

Level B: Are the words in a chapter of a fifth-grade book longer than the words in a chapter of a third-grade book?

Level C: Do fifth-grade books use longer words than third-grade books?

Popular Music Example

Level A: What type of music is most popular among students in our class?

Level B: How do the favorite types of music compare among different classes?

Level C: What type of music is most popular among students in our school?

Height and Arm Span Example

Level A: In our class, are the heights and arm spans of students approximately the same?

Level B: Is the relationship between arm span and height for the students in our class the same as the relationship between arm span and height for the students in another class?

Level C: Is height a useful predictor of arm span for the students in our school?

Plant Growth Example

Level A: Will a plant placed by the window grow taller than a plant placed away from the window?

Level B: Will five plants placed by the window grow taller than five plants placed away from the window?

Level C: How does the level of sunlight affect the growth of plants?

II. Collect Data

Word Length Example

Level A: How long are the words on this page?

The length of every word on the page is determined and recorded.

Level B: Are the words in a chapter of a fifth-grade book longer than the words in a chapter of a third-grade book?

A simple random sample of words from each chapter is used.

Level C: Do fifth-grade books use longer words than third-grade books?

Different sampling designs are considered and compared, and some are used. For example, rather than selecting a simple random sample of words, a simple random sample of pages from the book is selected and all the words on the chosen pages are used for the sample.

Note: At each level, issues of measurement should be addressed. The length of word depends on the definition of "word." For instance, is a number a word? Consistency of definition helps reduce measurement variability.

Plant Growth Example

Level A: Will a plant placed by the window grow taller than a plant placed away from the window?

A seedling is planted in a pot that is placed on the window sill. A second seedling of the same type and size is planted in a pot that is placed away from the window sill. After six weeks, the change in height for each is measured and recorded.

Level B: Will five plants of a particular type placed by the window grow taller than five plants of the same type placed away from the window?

Five seedlings of the same type and size are planted in a pan that is placed on the window sill. Five seedlings of the same type and size are planted in a pan that is placed away from the window sill. Random numbers are used to decide which plants go in the window. After six weeks, the change in height for each seedling is measured and recorded.

Level C: How does the level of sunlight affect the growth of plants?

Fifteen seedlings of the same type and size are selected. Three pans are used, with five of these seedlings planted in each. Fifteen seedlings of another variety are selected to determine if the effect of sunlight is the same on different types of plants. Five of these are planted in each of the three pans. The three pans are placed in locations with three different levels of light. Random numbers are used to decide which plants go in which pan. After six weeks, the change in height for each seedling is measured and recorded.

Note: At each level, issues of measurement should be addressed. The method of measuring change in height must be clearly understood and applied in order to reduce measurement variability.

III. Analyze Data

Popular Music Example

Level A: What type of music is most popular among students in our class?

A bar graph is used to display the number of students who choose each music category.

Level B: How do the favorite types of music compare among different classes?

For each class, a bar graph is used to display the percent of students who choose each music category. The same scales are used for both graphs so that they can easily be compared.

Level C: What type of music is most popular among students in our school?

A bar graph is used to display the percent of students who choose each music category. Because a random sample is used, an estimate of the margin of error is given.

Note: At each level, issues of measurement should be addressed. A questionnaire will be used to gather students' music preferences. The design and wording of the questionnaire must be carefully considered to avoid possible bias in the responses. The choice of music categories also could affect results.

Height and Arm Span Example

Level A: In our class, are the heights and arm spans of students approximately the same?

The difference between height and arm span is determined for each individual. An X-Y plot (scatterplot) is constructed with X = height, Y = arm span. The line Y = X is drawn on this graph.

Level B: Is the relationship between arm span and height for the students in our class the same as the relationship between arm span and height for the students in another class?

For each class, an X-Y plot is constructed with X = height, Y = arm span. An "eye ball" line is drawn on each graph to describe the relationship between height and arm span. The equation of this line is determined. An elementary measure of association is computed.

Level C: Is height a useful predictor of arm span for the students in our school?

The least squares regression line is determined and assessed for use as a prediction model.

Note: At each level, issues of measurement should be addressed. The methods used to measure height and arm span must be clearly understood and applied in order to reduce measurement variability. For instance, do we measure height with shoes on or off?

IV. Interpret Results

Word Length Example

Level A: How long are the words on this page?

The dotplot of all word lengths is examined and summarized. In particular, students will note the longest and shortest word lengths, the most common and least common lengths, and the length in the middle.

Level B: Are the words in a chapter of a fifth-grade book longer than the words in a chapter of a third-grade book?

Students interpret a comparison of the distribution of a sample of word lengths from the fifth-grade book with the distribution of word lengths from the third-grade book using a boxplot to represent each of these. The students also acknowledge that samples are being used that may or may not be representative of the complete chapters.

The boxplot for a sample of word lengths from the fifth-grade book is placed beside the boxplot of the sample from the third-grade book.

Level C: Do fifth-grade books use longer words than third-grade books?

The interpretation at Level C includes the interpretation at Level B, but also must consider generalizing from the books included in the study to a larger population of books.

Plant Growth Example

Level A: Will a plant placed by the window grow taller than a plant placed away from the window?

In this simple experiment, the interpretation is just a matter of comparing one measurement of change in size to another.

Level B: Will five plants placed by the window grow taller than five plants placed away from the window?

In this experiment, the student must interpret a comparison of one group of five measurements with another group. If a difference is noted, then the student acknowledges it is likely caused by the difference in light conditions.

Level C: How does the level of sunlight affect the growth of plants?

There are several comparisons of groups possible with this design. If a difference is noted, then the student acknowledges it is likely caused by the difference in light conditions or the difference in types of plants. It also is acknowledged that the randomization used in the experiment can result in some of the observed differences.

Nature of Variability

The focus on variability grows increasingly more sophisticated as students progress through the developmental levels.

Variability within a Group

This is the only type considered at Level A. In the word length example, differences among word lengths

> " The focus on variability grows increasingly more sophisticated as students progress through the developmental levels. "

on a single page are considered; this is variability within a group of word lengths. In the popular music example, differences in how many students choose each category of music are considered; this is variability within a group of frequencies.

Variability within a Group and Variability between Groups

At Level B, students begin to make comparisons of groups of measurements. In the word length example, a group of words from a fifth-grade book is compared to a group from a third-grade book. Such a comparison not only notes how much word lengths differ within each group, but must also take into consideration the differences between the two groups, such as the difference between median or mean word lengths.

Covariability

At Level B, students also begin to investigate the "statistical" relationship between two variables. The nature of this statistical relationship is described in terms of how the two variables "co-vary." In the height and arm span example, for instance, if the heights of two students differ by two centimeters, then we would like our model of the relationship to tell us by how much we might expect their arm spans to differ.

Variability in Model Fitting

At Level C, students assess how well a regression line will predict values of one variable from values of another variable using residual plots. In the height and arm span example, for instance, this assessment is based on examining whether differences between actual arm spans and the arm spans predicted by the model randomly vary about the horizontal line of "no difference" in the residual plot. Inference about a predicted value of y for a given value of x is valid only if the values of y vary at random according to a normal distribution centered on the regression line. Students at Level C learn to estimate this variability about the regression line using the estimated standard deviation of the residuals.

Induced Variability

In the plant growth example at Level B, the experiment is designed to determine if there will be a difference between the growth of plants in sunlight and of plants away from sunlight. We want to determine if an imposed difference on the environments will induce a difference in growth.

Sampling Variability

In the word length example at Level B, samples of words from a chapter are used. Students observe that two samples will produce different groups of word lengths. This is sampling variability.

Chance Variability from Sampling

When random selection is used, differences between samples will be due to chance. Understanding this chance variation is what leads to the predictability of results. In the popular music example, at Level C, this chance variation is not only considered, but is also the basis for understanding the concept of margin of error.

Chance Variability Resulting from Assignment to Groups in Experiments

In the plant growth example at Level C, plants are randomly assigned to groups. Students consider how this chance variation in random assignments might produce differences in results, although a formal analysis is not done.

Detailed Descriptions of Each Level

As this document transitions into detailed descriptions of each level, it is important to note that the examples selected for illustrating key concepts and the problem-solving process of statistical reasoning are based on real data and real-world contexts. *Those of you reading this document are stakeholders, and will need to be flexible in adapting these examples to fit your instructional circumstances.*

In This Section

→   Example 1: Choosing the Band
    for the End of the Year Party—
    Conducting a Survey

→   Comparing Groups

→   The Simple Experiment

→   Example 2: Growing Beans—
    A Simple Comparative Experiment

→   Making Use of Available Data

→   Describing Center and Spread

→   Looking for an Association

→   Example 3: Purchasing Sweatsuits—
    The Role of Height and Arm Span

→   Understanding Variability

→   The Role of Probability

→   Misuses of Statistics

→   Summary of Level A

Children are surrounded by data. They may think of data as a tally of students' preferences, such as favorite type of music, or as measurements, such as students' arm spans and number of books in school bags.

It is in Level A that children need to develop data sense—an understanding that data are more than just numbers. Statistics changes numbers into information.

Students should learn that data are generated with respect to particular contexts or situations and can be used to answer questions about the context or situation.

Opportunities should be provided for students to generate questions about a particular context (such as their classroom) and determine what data might be collected to answer these questions.

Students also should learn how to use basic statistical tools to analyze the data and make informal inferences in answering the posed questions.

Finally, students should develop basic ideas of probability in order to support their later use of probability in drawing inferences at Levels B and C.

It is preferable that students actually collect data, but not necessary in every case. Teachers should take advantage of naturally occurring situations in which students notice a pattern about some data and begin to raise questions. For example, when taking daily attendance one morning, students might note that many students are absent. The teacher could capitalize on this opportunity to have the students formulate questions that could be answered with attendance data.

Specifically, Level A recommendations in the Investigative Process include:

I. Formulate the Question

→ Teachers help pose questions (questions in contexts of interest to the student).

→ Students distinguish between statistical solution and fixed answer.

II. Collect Data to Answer the Question

→ Students conduct a census of the classroom.

→ Students understand individual-to-individual natural variability.

→ Students conduct simple experiments with nonrandom assignment of treatments.

→ Students understand induced variability attributable to an experimental condition.

III. Analyze the Data

→ Students compare individual to individual.

→ Students compare individual to a group.

→ Students become aware of group to group comparison.

→ Students understand the idea of a distribution.

→ Students describe a distribution.

→ Students observe association between two variables.

→ Students use tools for exploring distributions and association, including:

- Bar Graph
- Dotplot
- Stem and Leaf Plot
- Scatterplot
- Tables (using counts)
- Mean, Median, Mode, Range
- Modal Category

IV. Interpret Results

→ Students infer to the classroom.

→ Students acknowledge that results may be different in another class or group.

→ Students recognize the limitation of scope of inference to the classroom.

Example 1: Choosing the Band for the End of the Year Party—Conducting a Survey

Children at Level A may be interested in the favorite type of music among students at a certain grade level. An end of the year party is being planned and there is only enough money to hire one musical group. The class might investigate the question: *What type of music is most popular among students?*

This question attempts to measure a characteristic in the population of children at the grade level that will have the party. The characteristic, favorite music type, is a categorical variable—each child in that grade would be placed in a particular non-numerical category based on his or her favorite music type. The resulting data often are called *categorical data*.

The Level A class would most likely conduct a census of the students in a particular classroom to gauge what the favorite music type might be for the whole grade. At Level A, we want students to recognize that there will be individual-to-individual variability.

For example, a survey of 24 students in one of the classrooms at a particular grade level is taken. The data are summarized in the frequency table below. This *frequency table* is a *tabular representation* that takes Level A students to a summative level for categorical data. Students might first use *tally marks* to record the measurements of categorical data before finding frequencies (counts) for each category.

Table 2: Frequency Count Table

Favorite	Frequency or Count
Country	8
Rap	12
Rock	4

A Level A student might first use a *picture graph* to represent the tallies for each category. A picture graph uses a picture of some sort (such as a type of musical band) to represent each individual. Thus, each child who favors a particular music type would put a cut-out of that type of band directly onto the graph the teacher has created on the board. Instead of a picture of a band, another representation—such as a picture of a guitar, an X, or a colored square—can be used to represent each individual preference. A child who prefers "country" would go to the board and place a guitar, dot, X, or color in a square above the column labeled "country." In both cases, there is a deliberate recording of each data value, one at a time.

Note that a picture graph refers to a graph where an object, such as a construction paper cut-out, is used to represent one individual on the graph. (A cut-out of a tooth might be used to record how many teeth were lost by children in a kindergarten class each month.) The term *pictograph* often is used to refer to a graph in which a picture or symbol is used to represent several items that belong in the same category. For example, on a graph showing the distribution of car riders, walkers, and bus riders in a class, a cut-out of a school bus might be used to represent five bus riders. Thus, if the class had 13 bus riders, there would be approximately 2.5 busses on the graph.

This type of graph requires a basic understanding of proportional or multiplicative reasoning, and for this reason we do not advocate its use at Level A. Similarly, circle graphs require an understanding of proportional reasoning, so we do not advocate their use at Level A.

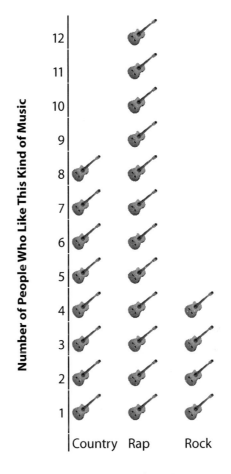

Figure 1: Picture graph of music preferences

A bar graph takes the student to the summative level with the data summarized from some other representation,

Students should understand that the mode is the category that contains the most data points, often referred to as the modal category.

such as a picture graph or a frequency count table. The bar on a bar graph is drawn as a rectangle, reaching up to the desired number on the *y*-axis.

A bar graph of students' music preferences is displayed below for the census taken of the classroom represented in the above frequency count table and picture graph.

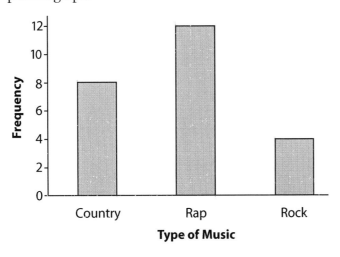

Figure 2: Bar graph of music preferences

Students at Level A should recognize the *mode* as a way to describe a "representative" or "typical" value for the distribution.

The mode is most useful for categorical data. Students should understand that the mode is the category that contains the most data points, often referred to as the *modal category*. In our favorite music example, rap music

was preferred by more children, thus the mode or modal category of the data set is rap music. Students could use this information to help the teachers in seeking a musical group for the end of the year party that specializes in rap music.

The vertical axis on the bar graph in Figure 2 could be scaled in terms of the proportion or percent of the sample for each category. As this involves proportional reasoning, converting frequencies to proportions (or percentages) will be developed in Level B.

Because most of the data collected at Level A will involve a census of the students' classroom, the first stage is for students to learn to read and interpret at a simple level what the data show about their own class. Reading and interpreting comes before inference. It is important to consider the question:

What might have caused the data to look like this?

It is also important for children to think about if and how their findings would *"scale up" to a larger group*, such as the entire grade level, the whole school, all children in the school system, all children in the state, or all people in the nation. They should note variables (such as age or geographic location) that might affect the data in the larger set. In the music example above, students might speculate that if they collected data on music preference from their teachers, the teachers might prefer a different type of music. Or, what would happen if they collected music preference from middle-school students in their school system? Level A students should begin recognizing the limitations of the scope of inference to a specific classroom.

Comparing Groups

Students at Level A may be interested in comparing two distinct groups with respect to some characteristic of those groups. For example, is there a difference between two groups—boys and girls—with respect to student participation in sports? The characteristic "participation in sports" is categorical (yes or no). The resulting categorical data for each gender may be analyzed using a frequency count table or bar graph. Another question Level A students might ask is whether there is a difference between boys and girls with respect to the distance they can jump, an example of taking measurements on a *numerical* variable. Data on numerical variables are obtained from situations that involve taking measurements, such as heights or temperatures, or situations in which objects are counted (e.g., determining the number of letters in your first name, the number of pockets on clothing worn by children in the class, or the number of siblings each child has). Such data often are called *numerical data*.

Returning to the question of comparing boys and girls with respect to jumping distance, students may measure the jumping distance for all of their classmates. Once the numerical data are gathered, the children might compare the lengths of girls' and boys' jumps

using a back-to-back ordered *stem and leaf plot*, such as the one below.

Girls		Boys
	8	
	7	
	6	1
	5	2 6 9
9 7 2	4	1 3 5 5 5
5 5 3 3 3 2 1	3	1 1 2 5 6 7
9 8 7 7 6 4 4 3 2	2	2 3 4 6
	1	

Inches Jumped in the Standing Broad Jump

Figure 3: Stem and leaf plot of jumping distances

From the stem and leaf plot, students can get a sense of shape—more symmetric for the boys than for the girls—and of the fact that boys tend to have longer jumps. Looking ahead to Level C, the previous examples of data collection design will be more formally discussed as examples of observational studies. The researcher has no control over which students go into the boy and girl groups (the pre-existing condition of gender defines the groups). The researcher then merely observes and collects measurements on characteristics within each group.

The Simple Experiment

Another type of design for collecting data appropriate at Level A is a *simple experiment*, which consists of taking measurements on a particular condition or group. Level A students may be interested in timing the swing of a pendulum or seeing how far a toy car runs off the end of a slope from a fixed starting position (future Pinewood Derby participants?) Also, measuring the same thing several times and finding a mean helps to lay the foundation for the fact that the mean has less variability as an estimate of the true mean value than does a single reading. This idea will be developed more fully at Level C.

Example 2: Growing Beans—A Simple Comparative Experiment

A *simple comparative experiment* is like a science experiment in which children compare the results of two or more conditions. For example, children might plant dried beans in soil and let them sprout, and then compare which one grows fastest—the one in the light or the one in the dark. The children decide which beans will be exposed to a particular type of lighting. The conditions to be compared here are the two types of lighting environments—light and dark. The type of lighting environment is an example of a categorical variable. Measurements of the plants' heights can be taken at the end of a specified time period to answer the question of whether one lighting environment is better for growing beans. The collected heights are an example of numerical data. In Level C, the concept of an experiment (where conditions are imposed by the researcher) will be more fully developed.

Another appropriate *graphical representation for numerical data on one variable* (in addition to the stem and leaf plot) at Level A is a *dotplot*. Both the dotplot and stem and leaf plot can be used to easily compare two or more similar sets of numerical data. In creating a dotplot, the *x*-axis should be labeled with a range of values that the numerical variable can assume. The *x*-axis for any one-variable graph conventionally is the axis representing the values of the variable under study. For example, in the bean growth experiment, children might record in a dotplot the height of beans (in centimeters) that were grown in the dark (labeled D) and in the light (labeled L) using a dotplot.

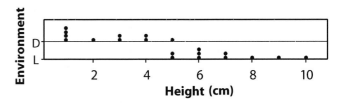

Figure 4: Dotplot of environment vs. height

It is obvious from the dotplot that the plants in the light environment tend to have greater heights than the plants in the dark environment.

Looking for clusters and gaps in the distribution helps students identify the *shape* of the distribution. Students should develop a sense of why a distribution takes on a particular shape for the context of the variable being considered.

→ Does the distribution have one main cluster (or mound) with smaller groups of similar size on each side of the cluster? If so, the distribution might be described as *symmetric*.

→ Does the distribution have one main cluster with smaller groups on each side that are not the same size? Students may classify this as "lopsided," or may use the term asymmetrical.

→ Why does the distribution take this shape? Using the dotplot from above, students will recognize both groups have distributions that are "lopsided," with the main cluster on the lower end of the distributions and a few values to the right of the main mound.

Making Use of Available Data

Most children love to eat hot dogs, but are aware that too much sodium is not necessarily healthy. Is there a difference in the sodium content of beef hot dogs (labeled B in Figure 5) and poultry hot dogs (labeled P in Figure 5)? To investigate this question, students can make use of available data. Using data from the June 1993 issue of *Consumer Reports* magazine, parallel dotplots can be constructed.

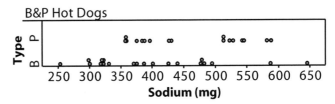

Figure 5: Parallel dotplot of sodium content

Students will notice that the distribution of the poultry hot dogs has two distinct clusters. What might explain the gap and two clusters? It could be another variable, such as the price of the poultry hot dogs, with more expensive hot dogs having less sodium. It can also be observed that the beef sodium amounts are more spread out (or vary more) than the poultry hot dogs. In addition, it appears the center of the distribution for the poultry hot dogs is higher than the center for the beef hot dogs.

As students advance to Level B, considering the shape of a distribution will lead to an understanding of what measures are appropriate for describing center and spread.

Describing Center and Spread

Students should understand that the *median* describes the center of a numerical data set in terms of how many data points are above and below it. The same number of data points (approximately half) lie to the left of the median and to the right of the median. Children can create a human graph to show how many letters are in their first names. All the children

"As students advance to Level B, considering the shape of a distribution will lead to an understanding of what measures are appropriate for describing center and spread."

with two-letter names can stand in a line, with all of the children having three-letter names standing in a parallel line. Once all children are assembled, the teacher can ask one child from each end of the graph to sit down, repeating this procedure until one child is left standing, representing the median. With Level A students, we advocate using an odd number of data points so the median is clear until students have mastered the idea of a midpoint.

Students should understand the *mean as a fair share* measure of center at Level A. In the name length example, the mean would be interpreted as "How long would our names be if they were all the same length?" This can be illustrated in small groups by having children take one snap cube for each letter in their name. In small groups, have students put all the cubes in the center of the table and redistribute them one at a time so each child has the same number. Depending on the children's experiences with fractions, they may say the mean name length is 4 R 2 or 4 1/2 or 4.5. Another example would be for the teacher to collect eight pencils of varying lengths from children and lay them end-to-end on the chalk rail. Finding the mean will answer the question "How long would each pencil be if they were all the same length?" That is, if we could glue all the pencils together and cut them into eight equal sections, how long would each section be? This can be modeled using adding machine tape (or string), by tearing off a piece of tape that is the same length as all eight pencils laid end-to-end.

Then, fold the tape in half three times to get eighths, showing the length of one pencil out of eight pencils of equal length. Both of these demonstrations can be mapped directly onto the algorithm for finding the mean: combine all data values (put all cubes in the middle, lay all pencils end-to-end and measure, add all values) and share fairly (distribute the cubes, fold the tape, and divide by the number of data values). Level A students should master the computation (by hand or using appropriate technology) of the mean so more sophisticated interpretations of the mean can be developed at Levels B and C.

The mean and median are *measures of location* for describing the center of a numerical data set. Determining the maximum and minimum values of a numerical data set assists children in describing the position of the smallest and largest value in a data set. In addition to describing the center of a data set, it is useful to know how the data vary or how spread out the data are.

One *measure of spread* for a distribution is the *range*, which is the difference between the maximum and minimum values. Measures of spread only make sense with numerical data.

In looking at the stem and leaf plot formed for the jumping distances (Figure 3), the range differs for boys (range = 39 inches) and girls (range = 27 inches). Girls are more consistent in their jumping distances than boys.

Looking for an Association

Students should be able to look at the possible *association of a numerical variable and a categorical variable* by comparing dotplots of a numerical variable disaggregated by a categorical variable. For example, using the parallel dotplots showing the growth habits of beans in the light and dark, students should look for similarities within each category and differences between the categories. As mentioned earlier, students should readily recognize from the dotplot that the beans grown in the light environment have grown taller overall, and therefore reason that it is best for beans to have a light environment. Measures of center and spread also can be compared. For example, students could calculate or make a visual estimate of the mean height of the beans grown in the light and the beans grown in the dark to substantiate their claim that light conditions are better for beans. They also might note that the range for plants grown in the dark is 4 cm, and 5 cm for plants grown in the light. Putting that information together with the mean should enable students to further solidify their conclusions about the advantages of growing beans in the light.

Considering the hot dog data, one general impression from the dotplot is that there is more variation in the sodium content for beef hot dogs. For beef hot dogs, the sodium content is between 250 mg and 650 mg, while for poultry hot dogs, the sodium content is between 350 mg and 600 mg. Neither the centers nor the shapes for the distributions are obvious from the dotplots. It is interesting to note the two apparent clusters of data for poultry hot dogs. Nine of the 17 poultry hot dogs have sodium content between 350 mg and 450 mg, while eight of the 17 poultry hot dogs have sodium content between 500 mg and 600 mg. A possible explanation for this division is that some poultry hot dogs are made from chicken, while others are made from turkey.

Example 3: Purchasing Sweat Suits—The Role of Height and Arm Span

What about the association between two numerical variables? Parent-teacher organizations at elementary schools have for a popular fund raiser "spirit wear," such as sweatshirts and sweatpants with the school name and mascot. The organizers need to have some guidelines about how many of each size garment to order. Should they offer the shirt and pants separately, or offer the sweatshirt and sweatpants as one outfit? Are the heights and arm spans of elementary students closely related, or do they differ considerably due to individual growing patterns of children? Thus, some useful questions to answer are:

Is there an association between height and arm span?
How strong is the association between height and arm span?

A *scatterplot* can be used to graphically represent data when values of two numerical variables are obtained from the same individual or object. Can we use height

" With the use of a scatterplot, Level A students can visually look for trends and patterns. "

to predict a person's arm span? Students can measure each other's heights and arm spans, and then construct a scatterplot to look for a relationship between these two numerical variables. Data on height and arm span are measured (in centimeters) for 26 students. The data presented below are for college students and are included for illustrative purposes.

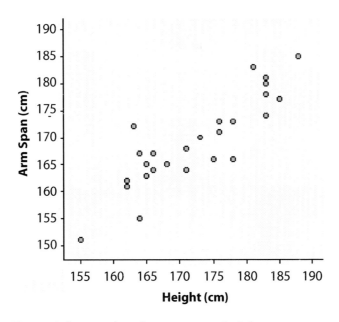

Figure 6: Scatterplot of arm span vs. height

With the use of a scatterplot, Level A students can visually *look for trends and patterns.*

For example, in the arm span versus height scatterplot above, students should be able to identify the consistent relationship between the two variables: generally as one gets larger, so does the other. Based on these data, the organizers might feel comfortable ordering some complete outfits of sweatshirt and sweatpants based on sizes. However, some students may need to order the sweatshirt and sweatpants separately based on sizes. Another important question the organizers will need to ask is whether this sample is representative of all the students in the school. How was the sample chosen?

Students at Level A also can use a scatterplot to graphically look at the values of a numerical variable change over time, referred to as a *time plot.* For example, children might chart the outside temperature at various times during the day by recording the values themselves or by using data from a newspaper or the internet.

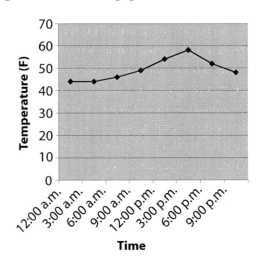

Figure 7: Timeplot of temperature vs. time

When students advance to Level B, they will quantify these trends and patterns with measures of association.

Understanding Variability

Students should explore possible reasons data look the way they do and *differentiate between variation and error*. For example, in graphing the colors of candies in a small packet, children might expect the colors to be evenly distributed (or they may know from prior experience that they are not). Children could speculate about why certain colors appear more or less frequently due to variation (e.g., cost of dyes, market research on people's preferences, etc.). Children also could identify possible places where errors could have occurred in their handling of the data/candies (e.g., dropped candies, candies stuck in bag, eaten candies, candies given away to others, colors not recorded because they don't match personal preference, miscounting). Teachers should capitalize on *naturally occurring "errors"* that happen when collecting data in the classroom and help students speculate about the *impact of these errors* on the final results. For example, when asking students to vote for their favorite food, it is common for students to vote twice, to forget to vote, to record their vote in the wrong spot, to misunderstand what is being asked, to change their mind, or to want to vote for an option that is not listed. Counting errors are also common among young children, which can lead to incorrect tallies of data points in categories. Teachers can help students think about how these events might affect the final outcome if only one person did this, if several people did it, or if many people did it. Students can generate additional examples of ways errors might occur in a particular data-gathering situation.

The notions of error and variability should be used to explain the outliers, clusters, and gaps students observe in the graphical representations of the data. An understanding of error versus natural variability will help students interpret whether an outlier is a legitimate data value that is unusual or whether the outlier is due to a recording error.

At Level A, it is imperative that students begin to understand the concept of variability. As students move from Level A to Level B to Level C, it is important to always keep at the forefront that *understanding variability is the essence of developing data sense*.

The Role of Probability

Level A students need to develop basic ideas of probability in order to support their later use of probability in drawing inferences at Levels B and C.

At Level A, students should understand that *probability is a measure of the chance that something will happen. It is a measure of certainty or uncertainty*. Events should be seen as lying on a continuum from impossible to certain, with less likely, equally likely, and more likely lying in between. Students learn to informally assign numbers to the likelihood that something will occur.

An example of assigning numbers on a number line is given below:

0	¼	½	¾	1
Impossible	Unlikely or less likely	Equally likely to occur and not occur	Likely or more likely	Certain

Students should have experiences *estimating probabilities using empirical data.* Through experimentation (or simulation), students should develop an explicit understanding of the notion that the more times you repeat a random phenomenon, the closer the results will be to the expected mathematical model. At Level A, we are considering only simple models based on equally likely outcomes or, at the most, something based on this, such as the sum of the faces on two number cubes. For example, very young children can state that a penny should land on heads half the time and on tails half the time when flipped. The student has given the expected model and probability for tossing a head or tail, assuming that the coin is "fair."

If a child flips a penny 10 times to obtain empirical data, it is quite possible he or she will not get five heads and five tails. However, if the child flips the coin hundreds of times, we would expect to see that results will begin *stabilizing* to the expected probabilities of .5 for heads and .5 for tails. This is known as the *Law of Large Numbers.* Thus, at

Level A, probability experiments should focus on obtaining empirical data to develop relative frequency interpretations that children can easily translate to models with known and understandable "mathematical" probabilities. The classic flipping coins, spinning simple spinners, and tossing number cubes are reliable tools to use in helping Level A students develop an understanding of probability. The concept of relative frequency interpretations will be important at Level B when the student works with proportional reasoning—going from counts or frequencies to proportions or percentages.

As students work with results from repeating random phenomena, they can develop an understanding for the concept of *randomness.* They will see that when flipping a coin 10 times, although we would expect five heads and five tails, the actual results will vary from one student to the next. They also will see that if a head results on one toss, that doesn't mean the next flip will result in a tail. Because coin tossing is a random experiment, there is always uncertainty as to how the coin will land from one toss to the next. However, at Level A, students can begin to develop the notion that although we have uncertainty and variability in our results, by examining what happens to the random process in the *long run,* we can quantify the uncertainty and variability with probabilities—giving a predictive number for the likelihood of an outcome in the long run. At Level B, students will see the role probability plays in the development of the concept of the simple random sample and the role probability plays with randomness.

Misuses of Statistics

The Level A student should learn that proper use of statistical terminology is as important as the proper use of statistical tools. In particular, the proper use of the mean and median should be emphasized. These numerical summaries are appropriate for describing numerical variables, not categorical variables. For example, when collecting categorical data on favorite type of music, the *number* of children in the sample who prefer each type of music is summarized as a frequency. It is easy to confuse categorical and numerical data in this case and try to find the mean or median of the frequencies for favorite type of music. However, one cannot use the frequency counts to compute a mean or median for a categorical variable. The frequency counts *are* the numerical summary for the categorical variable.

Another common mistake for the Level A student is the inappropriate use of a bar graph with numerical data. A bar graph is used to summarize categorical data. If a variable is numerical, the appropriate graphical display with bars is called a *histogram*, which is introduced in Level B. At Level A, appropriate graphical displays for numerical data are the dotplot and the stem and leaf plot.

Summary of Level A

If students become comfortable with the ideas and concepts described above, they will be prepared to further develop and enhance their understanding of the key concepts for data sense at Level B.

It is also important to recognize that helping students develop data sense at Level A allows mathematics instruction to be driven by data. The traditional mathematics strands of algebra, functions, geometry, and measurement all can be developed with the use of data. Making sense of data should be an integrated part of the mathematics curriculum, starting in pre-kindergarten.

In This Section

→ Example 1, Level A Revisited: Choosing a Band for the School Dance

→ Connecting Two Categorical Variables

→ Questionnaires and Their Difficulties

→ Measure of Location—The Mean as a Balance Point

→ A Measure of Spread—The Mean Absolute Deviation

→ Representing Data Distributions— The Frequency Table and Histogram

→ Comparing Distributions— The Boxplot

→ Measuring the Strength of Association between Two Quantitative Variables

→ Modeling Linear Association

→ The Importance of Random Selection

→ Comparative Experiments

→ Time Series

→ Misuses of Statistics

→ Summary of Level B

Level B

Instruction at Level B should build on the statistical base developed at Level A and set the stage for statistics at Level C. Instructional activities at Level B should continue to emphasize the four main components in the investigative process and have the spirit of genuine statistical practice. Students who complete Level B should see statistical reasoning as a process for solving problems through data and quantitative reasoning.

At Level B, students become more aware of the statistical question distinction (a question with an answer based on data that vary versus a question with a deterministic answer). They also should make decisions about what variables to measure and how to measure them in order to address the question posed.

Students should use and expand the graphical, tabular, and numerical summaries introduced at Level A to investigate more sophisticated problems. Also, when selecting a sample, students should develop a basic understanding of the role probability plays in random selection—and in random assignment when conducting an experiment.

At Level B, students investigate problems with more emphasis placed on possible associations among two or more variables and understand how a more sophisticated collection of graphical, tabular, and numerical summaries is used to address these questions. Finally, students recognize ways in which statistics is used or misused in their world.

Specifically, Level B recommendations in the *Investigative Process* include:

I. Formulate Questions

→   Students begin to pose their own questions.

→   Students address questions involving a group larger than their classroom and begin to recognize the distinction among a population, a census, and a sample.

II. Collect Data

→   Students conduct censuses of two or more classrooms.

→   Students design and conduct nonrandom sample surveys and begin to use random selection.

→   Students design and conduct comparative experiments and begin to use random assignment.

III. Analyze Data

→   Students expand their understanding of a data distribution.

→   Students quantify variability within a group.

→   Students compare two or more distributions using graphical displays and numerical summaries.

→ Students use more sophisticated tools for summarizing and comparing distributions, including:

- Histograms
- The IQR (Interquartile Range) and MAD (Mean Absolute Deviation)
- Five-Number Summaries and boxplots

→ Students acknowledge sampling error.

→ Students quantify the strength of association between two variables, develop simple models for association between two numerical variables, and use expanded tools for exploring association, including:

- Contingency tables for two categorical variables
- Time series plots
- The QCR (Quadrant Count Ratio) as a measure of strength of association
- Simple lines for modeling association between two numerical variables

IV. Interpret Results

→ Students describe differences between two or more groups with respect to center, spread, and shape.

→ Students acknowledge that a sample may not be representative of a larger population.

→ Students understand basic interpretations of measures of association.

→ Students begin to distinguish between an observational study and a designed experiment.

→ Students begin to distinguish between "association" and "cause and effect."

→ Students recognize sampling variability in summary statistics, such as the sample mean and the sample proportion.

Example 1, Level A Revisited: Choosing a Band for the School Dance

Many of the graphical, tabular, and numerical summaries introduced at Level A can be enhanced and used to investigate more sophisticated problems at Level B. Let's revisit the problem of planning for the school dance introduced in Level A, in which, by conducting a census of the class, a Level A class investigated the question:

What type of music is most popular among students?

Recall that the class was considered to be the entire population, and data were collected on every member of the population. A similar investigation at Level B would include recognition that one class may not be representative of the opinions of all students at the school. Level B students might want to compare the opinions of their class with the opinions of other classes from their school. A Level B class might investigate the questions:

What type of music is most popular among students at our school?

How do the favorite types of music differ between classes?

As class sizes may be different, results should be summarized with relative frequencies or percents in order to make comparisons. Percentages are useful in that they allow us to think of having comparable results for groups of size 100. Level B students will see more emphasis on proportional reasoning throughout the mathematics curriculum, and they should be comfortable summarizing and interpreting data in terms of percents or fractions.

Table 3: Frequencies and Relative Frequencies

Class 1		
Favorite	Frequency	Relative Frequency Percentage
Country	8	33%
Rap	12	50%
Rock	4	17%
Total	**24**	**100%**
Class 2		
Favorite	Frequency	Relative Frequency Percentage
Country	5	17%
Rap	11	37%
Rock	14	47%
Total	**30**	**101%**

The results from two classes are summarized in Table 3 using both frequency and relative frequency (percents).

The bar graph below compares the percent of each favorite music category for the two classes.

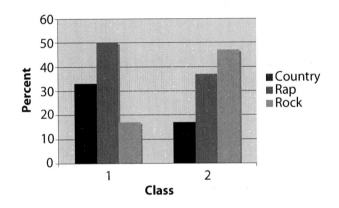

Figure 8: Comparative bar graph for music preferences

Students at Level B should begin to recognize that there is not only variability from one individual to another within a group, but also in results from one group to another. This second type of variability is illustrated by the fact that the most popular music is rap music in Class 1, while it is rock music in Class 2. That is, the mode for Class 1 is rap music, while the mode for Class 2 is rock music.

The results from the two samples might be combined in order to have a larger sample of the entire school. The combined results indicate rap music is the favorite type of music for 43% of the students, rock music is preferred by 33%, while only 24% of the students selected country music as their favorite. Level B students should recognize that although this is a larger sample, it still may not be representative of the entire population (all students at their school). In statistics, randomness and probability are incorporated into the sample selection procedure in order to provide a method that is "fair" and to improve the chances of selecting a representative sample. For example, if the class decides to select what is called a simple random sample of 54 students, then each possible sample of 54 students has the same probability of being selected. This application illustrates one of the roles of probability in statistics. Although Level B students may not actually employ a random selection procedure when collecting data, issues related to obtaining representative samples should be discussed at this level.

Connecting Two Categorical Variables

As rap was the most popular music for the two combined classes, the students might argue for a rap group for the dance. However, more than half of those surveyed preferred either rock or country music. Will these students be unhappy if a rap band is chosen? Not necessarily, as many students who like rock music also may like rap music. To investigate this problem, students might explore two additional questions:

Do students who like rock music tend to like or dislike rap music?

Do students who like country music tend to like or dislike rap music?

To address these questions, the survey should ask students not only their favorite type of music, but also whether they like rap, rock, and country music.

The *two-way frequency table* (or *contingency table*) below provides a way to investigate possible connections between two categorical variables.

Table 4: Two-Way Frequency Table

		Like Rap Music?		
		Yes	No	Row Totals
Like Rock Music?	Yes	27	6	33
	No	4	17	21
Column Totals		31	23	54

According to these results, of the 33 students who liked rock music, 27 also liked rap music. That is, 82% (27/33) of the students who like rock music also like rap music. This indicates that students who like rock music tend to like rap music as well. Once again, notice the use of proportional reasoning in interpreting these results. A similar analysis could be performed to determine if students who like country tend to like or dislike rap music. A more detailed discussion of this example and a measure of association between two categorical variables is given in the Appendix for Level B.

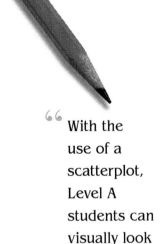

" With the use of a scatterplot, Level A students can visually look for trends and patterns. "

Questionnaires and Their Difficulties

At Level B, students should begin to learn about surveys and the many pitfalls to avoid when designing and conducting them. One issue involves the wording of questions. Questions must be unambiguous and easy to understand. For example, the question:

Are you against the school implementing a no-door policy on bathroom stalls?

is worded in a confusing way. An alternative way to pose this question is:

The school is considering implementing a no-door policy on bathroom stalls. What is your opinion regarding this policy?

Strongly Oppose   Oppose   No Opinion   Support   Strongly Support

Questions should avoid leading the respondent to an answer. For example, the question:

Since our football team hasn't had a winning season in 20 years and is costing the school money, rather than generating funds, do you feel we should concentrate more on another sport, such as soccer or basketball?

is worded in a way that is biased against the football team.

The responses to questions with coded responses should include all possible answers, and the answers should not overlap. For example, for the question:

How much time do you spend studying at home on a typical night?

the responses:

none   1 hour or less   1 hour or more

would confuse a student who spends one hour a night studying.

There are many other considerations about question formulation and conducting sample surveys that can be introduced at Level B. Two such issues are how the interviewer asks the questions and how accurately the responses are recorded. It is important for students to realize that the conclusions from their study depend on the accuracy of their data.

Measure of Location—The Mean as a Balance Point

Another idea developed at Level A that can be expanded at Level B is the mean as a numerical summary of center for a collection of numerical data. At Level A, the mean is interpreted as the "fair share" value for data. That is, the mean is the value you would get if all the data from subjects are combined and then evenly redistributed so each subject's value is the same. Another interpretation of the mean is that it is the balance point of the corresponding data distribution. Here is an outline of an activity that illustrates the notion of the mean as a balance point. Nine students were asked:

How many pets do you have?

The resulting data were 1, 3, 4, 4, 4, 5, 7, 8, 9. These data are summarized in the dotplot shown in Figure 9. Note that in the actual activity, stick-on notes were used as "dots" instead of Xs.

> " At Level A, the mean is interpreted as the 'fair share' value for data. "

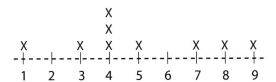

Figure 9: Dotplot for pet count

If the pets are combined into one group, there are a total of 45 pets. If the pets are evenly redistributed among the nine students, then each student would get five pets. That is, the mean number of pets is five. The dotplot representing the result that all nine students have exactly five pets is shown below:

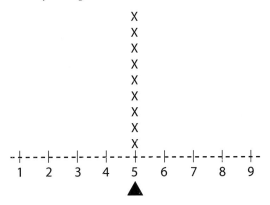

Figure 10: Dotplot showing pets evenly distributed

It is hopefully obvious that if a pivot is placed at the value 5, then the horizontal axis will "balance" at this pivot point. That is, the "balance point" for the horizontal axis for this dotplot is 5. What is the balance point for the dotplot displaying the original data?

We begin by noting what happens if one of the dots over 5 is removed and placed over the value 7, as shown below:

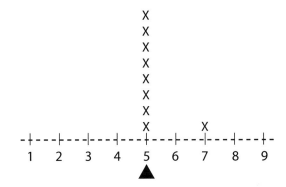

Figure 11: Dotplot with one data point moved

Clearly, if the pivot remains at 5, the horizontal axis will tilt to the right. What can be done to the remaining dots over 5 to "rebalance" the horizontal axis at the pivot point? Since 7 is two units *above* 5, one solution is to move a dot two units *below* 5 to 3, as shown below:

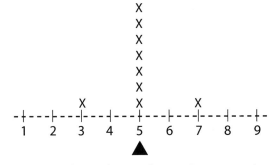

Figure 12: Dotplot with two data points moved

The horizontal axis is now rebalanced at the pivot point. Is this the only way to rebalance the axis at 5? No. Another way to rebalance the axis at the pivot point would be to move two dots from 5 to 4, as shown below:

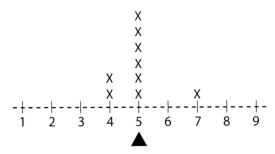

Figure 13: Dotplot with different data points moved

The horizontal axis is now rebalanced at the pivot point. That is, the "balance point" for the horizontal axis for this dotplot is 5. Replacing each "X" (dot) in this plot with the distance between the value and 5, we have:

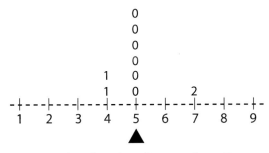

Figure 14: Dotplot showing distance from 5

Notice that the total distance for the two values below the 5 (the two 4s) is the same as the total distance for

the one value above the 5 (the 7). For this reason, the balance point of the horizontal axis is 5. Replacing each value in the dotplot of the original data by its distance from 5 yields the following plot:

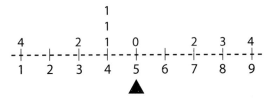

Figure 15: Dotplot showing original data and distance from 5

The total distance for the values below 5 is 9, the same as the total distance for the values above 5. For this reason, the mean (5) is the balance point of the horizontal axis.

Both the mean and median often are referred to as *measures of central location*. At Level A, the median also was introduced as the quantity that has the same number of data values on each side of it in the ordered data. This "sameness of each side" is the reason the median is a measure of central location. The previous activity demonstrates that the total distance for the values below the mean is the same as the total distance for the values above the mean, and illustrates why the mean also is considered to be a measure of central location.

A Measure of Spread—The Mean Absolute Deviation

Statistics is concerned with variability in data. One important idea is to quantify how much variability exists in a collection of numerical data. Quantities that measure the degree of variability in data are called *measures of spread*. At Level A, students are introduced to the *range* as a measure of spread in numerical data. At Level B, students should be introduced to the idea of comparing data values to a central value, such as the mean or median, and quantifying how different the data are from this central value.

In the number of pets example, how different are the original data values from the mean? One way to measure the degree of variability from the mean is to determine the total distance of all values from the mean. Using the final dotplot from the previous example, the total distance the nine data values are from the mean of 5 pets is 18 pets. The magnitude of this quantity depends on several factors, including the number of measurements. To adjust for the number of measurements, the total distance from the mean is divided by the number of measurements. The resulting quantity is called the *Mean Absolute Deviation,* or MAD. The MAD is the average distance of each data value from the mean. That is:

$$MAD = \frac{\text{Total Distance from the Mean for all Values}}{\text{Number of Data Values}}$$

The MAD for the data on number of pets from the previous activity is:

$$MAD = 18/9 = 2$$

The MAD indicates that the actual number of pets for the nine students differs from the mean of five pets by two pets, on average. Kader (1999) gives a thorough discussion of this activity and the MAD.

The MAD is an indicator of spread based on all the data and provides a measure of average variation in the data from the mean. The MAD also serves as a precursor to the standard deviation, which will be developed at Level C.

Representing Data Distributions—The Frequency Table and Histogram

At Level B, students should develop additional tabular and graphical devices for representing data distributions of numerical variables. Several of these build upon representations developed at Level A. For example, students at Level B might explore the problem of placing an order for hats. To prepare an order, one needs to know which hat sizes are most common and which occur least often. To obtain information about hat sizes, it is necessary to measure head circumferences. European hat sizes are based on the metric system. For example, a European hat size of 55 is designed to fit a person with a head circumference of between 550 mm and 559 mm. In planning an order for adults, students might collect preliminary data on the head circumferences of their parents, guardians, or other adults. Such data would be the result of a nonrandom sample. The data summarized in the following stemplot (also known as stem and leaf plot) are head circumferences measured in millimeters for a sample of 55 adults.

51 | 3

52 | 5

53 | 133455

54 | 2334699

55 | 12222345

56 | 0133355588

57 | 113477

58 | 02334458

59 | 1558

60 | 13

61 | 28

51 | 3 means 513 mm

Figure 16: Stemplot of head circumference

Based on the stemplot, some head sizes do appear to be more common than others. Head circumferences in the 560s are most common. Head circumferences fall off in a somewhat symmetric manner on both sides of the 560s, with very few smaller than 530 mm or larger than 600 mm.

In practice, a decision of how many hats to order would be based on a much larger sample, possibly hundreds or even thousands of adults. If a larger sample was available, a stemplot would not be a practical device for summarizing the data distribution. An alternative to the stemplot is to form a distribution based on dividing the data into groups or intervals. This method can be illustrated through a smaller data set, such as the 55 head circumferences, but is applicable for larger data sets as well. The *grouped frequency* and *grouped relative frequency* distributions and the *relative frequency histogram* that correspond to the above stemplot are:

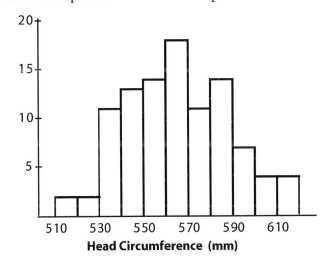

Figure 17: Relative frequency histogram

45

Table 5: Grouped Frequency and Grouped Relative Frequency Distributions

Stem	Limits on Recorded Measurements on Head Circumference	Interval of Actual Head Circumferences	Frequency	Relative Frequency (%)
51	510–519	510–<520	1	1.8
52	520–529	520–<530	1	1.8
53	530–539	530–<540	6	10.9
54	540–549	540–<550	7	12.7
55	550–559	550–<560	8	14.5
56	560–569	560–<570	10	18.2
57	570–579	570–<580	6	10.9
58	580–589	580–<590	8	14.5
59	590–599	590–<600	4	7.3
60	600–609	600–<610	2	3.6
61	610–619	610–<620	2	3.6
		Total	55	99.8

If the hat manufacturer requires that orders be in multiples of 250 hats, then based on the above results, how many hats of each size should be ordered? Using the relative frequency distribution, the number of hats of each size for an order of 250 hats is shown in Table 6.

Once again, notice how students at Level B would utilize proportional reasoning to determine the number of each size to order. Kader and Perry (1994) give a detailed description of "The Hat Shop" problem.

Comparing Distributions—The Boxplot

Problems that require comparing distributions for two or more groups are common in statistics. For example, at Level A students compared the amount of sodium in beef and poultry hot dogs by examining parallel dotplots. At Level B, more sophisticated representations should be developed for comparing distributions. One of the most useful graphical devices for comparing distributions of numerical data is the *boxplot*. The boxplot (also called a box-and-whiskers

Table 6: Hat Size Data

Hat Size	Number to Order
51	5
52	5
53	27
54	32
55	36
56	46
57	27
58	36
59	18
60	9
61	9

Table 7: Five-Number Summaries for Sodium Content

	Beef Hot Dogs (n = 20)	Poultry Hot Dogs (n = 17)
Minimum	253	357
First Quartile	320.5	379
Median	380.5	430
Third Quartile	478	535
Maximum	645	588

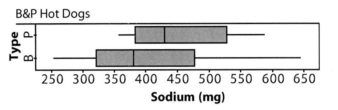

Figure 18: Boxplot for sodium content

plot) is a graph based on a division of the ordered data into four groups, with the same number of data values in each group (approximately one-fourth). The four groups are determined from the *Five-Number Summary* (the minimum data value, the first quartile, the median, the third quartile, and the maximum data value). The Five-Number Summaries and comparative boxplots for the data on sodium content for beef (labeled B) and poultry (labeled P) hot dogs introduced in Level A are given in Table 7 and Figure 18.

Interpreting results based on such an analysis requires comparisons based on global characteristics of each distribution (center, spread, and shape). For example, the median sodium content for poultry hot dogs is

430 mg, almost 50 mg more than the median sodium content for beef hot dogs. The medians indicate that a typical value for the sodium content of poultry hot dogs is greater than a typical value for beef hot dogs. The range for the beef hot dogs is 392 mg, versus 231 mg for the poultry hot dogs. The ranges indicate that, overall, there is more spread (variation) in the sodium content of beef hot dogs than poultry hot dogs. Another measure of spread that should be introduced at Level B is the *interquartile range,* or IQR. The IQR is the difference between the third and first quartiles, and indicates the range of the middle 50% of the data. The IQRs for sodium content are 157.5 mg for

beef hot dogs and 156 mg for poultry hot dogs. The IQRs suggest that the spread within the middle half of data for beef hot dogs is similar to the spread within the middle half of data for poultry hot dogs. The boxplots also suggest that each distribution is somewhat skewed right. That is, each distribution appears to have somewhat more variation in the upper half. Considering the degree of variation in the data and the amount of overlap in the boxplots, a difference of 50 mg between the medians is not really that large. Finally, it is interesting to note that more than 25% of beef hot dogs have less sodium than all poultry hot dogs. On the other hand, the highest sodium levels are for beef hot dogs.

Note that there are several variations of boxplots. At Level C, performing an analysis using boxplots might include a test for *outliers* (values that are extremely large or small when compared to the variation in the majority of the data). If outliers are identified, they often are detached from the "whiskers" of the plot. Outlier analysis is not recommended at Level B, so whiskers extend to the minimum and maximum data values. However, Level B students may encounter outliers when using statistical software or graphing calculators.

Measuring the Strength of Association between Two Quantitative Variables

At Level B, more sophisticated data representations should be developed for the investigation of problems

Table 8: Height and Arm Span Data

Height	Arm Span	Height	Arm Span
155	151	173	170
162	162	175	166
162	161	176	171
163	172	176	173
164	167	178	173
164	155	178	166
165	163	181	183
165	165	183	181
166	167	183	178
166	164	183	174
168	165	183	180
171	164	185	177
171	168	188	185

that involve the examination of the relationship between two numeric variables. At Level A, the problem of packaging sweat suits (shirt and pants together or separate) was examined through a study of the relationship between height and arm span. There are several statistical questions related to this problem that can be addressed at Level B with a more in-depth analysis of the height/arm span data. For example:

How strong is the association between height and arm span?

Is height a useful predictor of arm span?

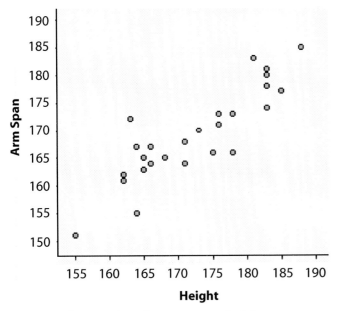

Figure 19: Scatterplot of arm span vs. height

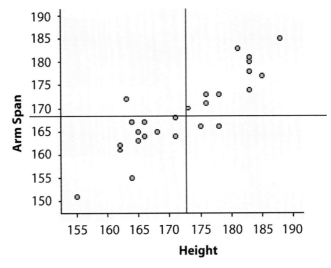

Figure 20: Scatterplot showing means

Table 8 provides data on height and arm span (measured in centimeters) for 26 students. For convenience, the data on height have been ordered.

The height and arm span data are displayed in Figure 19. The scatterplot suggests a fairly strong increasing relationship between height and arm span. In addition, the relationship appears to be quite linear.

Measuring the strength of association between two variables is an important statistical concept that should be introduced at Level B. The scatterplot in Figure 20 for the height/arm span data includes a vertical line drawn through the mean height ($x = 172.5$) and a horizontal line drawn through the mean arm span ($y = 169.3$).

The two lines divide the scatterplot into four regions (or quadrants). The upper right region (Quadrant 1) contains points that correspond to individuals with above average height and above average arm span. The upper left region (Quadrant 2) contains points that correspond to individuals with below average height and above average arm span. The lower left region (Quadrant 3) contains points that correspond to individuals with below average height and below average arm span. The lower right region (Quadrant

4) contains points that correspond to individuals with above average height and below average arm span.

Notice that most points in the scatterplot are in either Quadrant 1 or Quadrant 3. That is, most people with above average height also have above average arm span (Quadrant 1) and most people with below average height also have below average arm span (Quadrant 3). One person has below average height with above average arm span (Quadrant 2) and two people have above average height with below average arm span (Quadrant 4). These results indicate that there is a *positive association* between the variables *height* and *arm span*. Generally stated, two numeric variables are *positively associated* when above average values of one variable tend to occur with above average values of the other and when below average values of one variable tend to occur with below average values of the other. *Negative association* between two numeric variables occurs when below average values of one variable tend to occur with above average values of the other and when above average values of one variable tend to occur with below average values of the other.

A *correlation coefficient* is a quantity that measures the direction and strength of an association between two variables. Note that in the previous example, points in Quadrants 1 and 3 contribute to the positive association between height and arm span, and there is a total of 23 points in these two quadrants. Points in Quadrants 2 and 4 do not contribute to the positive

association between height and arm span, and there is a total of three points in these two quadrants. One correlation coefficient between height and arm span is given by the QCR (*Quadrant Count Ratio*):

$$QCR = \frac{23 - 3}{26} = .77$$

A QCR of .77 indicates that there is a fairly strong positive association between the two variables height and arm span. This indicates that a person's height is a useful predictor of his/her arm span.

In general, the QCR is defined as:

The QCR has the following properties:

(Number of Points in Quadrants 1 and 3)
− (Number of Points in Quadrants 2 and 4)

Number of Points in all Four Quadrants

→   The QCR is unitless.

→   The QCR is always between −1 and +1 inclusive.

Holmes (2001) gives a detailed discussion of the QCR. A similar correlation coefficient for 2x2 contingency tables is described in Conover (1999) and discussed in the Appendix for Level B. The QCR is a measure of the strength of association based on only the number of points in each quadrant and, like most summary measures, has its shortcomings. At Level C, the shortcomings of the QCR can be

> **A correlation coefficient is a quantity that measures the direction and strength of an association between two variables.**

addressed and used as foundation for developing Pearson's correlation coefficient.

Modeling Linear Association

The height/arm span data were collected at Level A in order to study the problem of packaging sweat suits. Should a shirt and pants be packaged separately or together? A QCR of .77 suggests a fairly strong positive association between height and arm span, which indicates that height is a useful predictor of arm span and that a shirt and pants could be packaged together. If packaged together, how can a person decide which size sweat suit to buy? Certainly, the pant-size of a sweat suit depends on a person's height and the shirt-size depends on a person's arm span. As many people know their height, but may not know their arm span, can height be used to help people decide which size sweat suit they wear? Specifically:

Can the relationship between height and arm span be described using a linear function?

Students at Level B will study linear relationships in other areas of their mathematics curriculum. The degree to which these ideas have been developed will determine how we might proceed at this point. For example, if students have not yet been introduced to the equation of a line, then they simply might draw a line through the "center of the data" as shown in Figure 21.

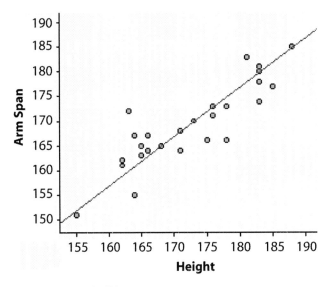

Figure 21: Eyeball line

This line can be used to predict a person's arm span if his or her height is known. For example, to predict the arm span for a person who is 170 cm tall, a vertical segment is drawn up from the X-axis at Height = 170. At the point this vertical segment intersects the segment, a horizontal line is drawn to the Y-axis. The value where this horizontal segment intersects the Y-axis is the predicted arm span. Based on the graph above, it appears that we would predict an arm span of approximately 167 cm for a person who is 170 cm tall.

If students are familiar with the equation for a line and know how to find the equation from two points, then they might use the Mean – Mean line, which is determined as follows. Order the data according to the X-coordinates and divide the data into two "halves" based on this ordering. If there is an odd number of measurements, remove the middle point from the analysis. Determine the means for the X-coordinates and Y-coordinates in each half and find the equation of the line that passes through these two points. Using the previous data:

Lower Half (13 Points)	Upper Half (13 Points)
Mean Height = 164.8	Mean Height = 180.2
Mean Arm Span = 163.4	Mean Arm Span = 175.2

The equation of the line that goes through the points (164.8, 163.4) and (180.2, 175.2) is Predicted Arm Span ≈ 37.1 + .766(Height). This equation can be used to predict a person's height more accurately than an eyeball line. For example, if a person is 170 cm tall, then we would predict his/her height to be approximately 37.1 + .766(170) = 167.3 cm. A more sophisticated approach (least squares) to determine a "best-fitting" line through the data will be introduced in Level C.

The Importance of Random Selection

In statistics, we often want to extend results beyond a particular group studied to a larger group, the *population*. We are trying to gain information about the population by examining a portion of the population, called a *sample*. Such generalizations are valid only if the data are representative of that larger group. A representative sample is one in which the relevant characteristics of the sample members are generally the same as those of the population. Improper or biased sample selection tends to systematically favor certain outcomes, and can produce misleading results and erroneous conclusions.

Random sampling is a way to remove bias in sample selection, and tends to produce representative samples. At Level B, students should experience the consequences of nonrandom selection and develop a basic understanding of the principles involved in random selection procedures. Following is a description of an activity that allows students to compare sample results based on personal (nonrandom) selection versus sample results based on random selection.

Consider the 80 circles on the next page. What is the average diameter for these 80 circles? Each student should take about 15 seconds and select five circles that he/she thinks best represent the sizes of the 80 circles. After selecting the sample, each student should find the average diameter for the circles in her/his personal sample. Note that the diameter is 1 cm for the small circles, 2 cm for the medium-sized circles, and 3 cm for the large circles.

Next, each student should number the circles from one to 80 and use a random digit generator to select a random sample of size five. Each student should find

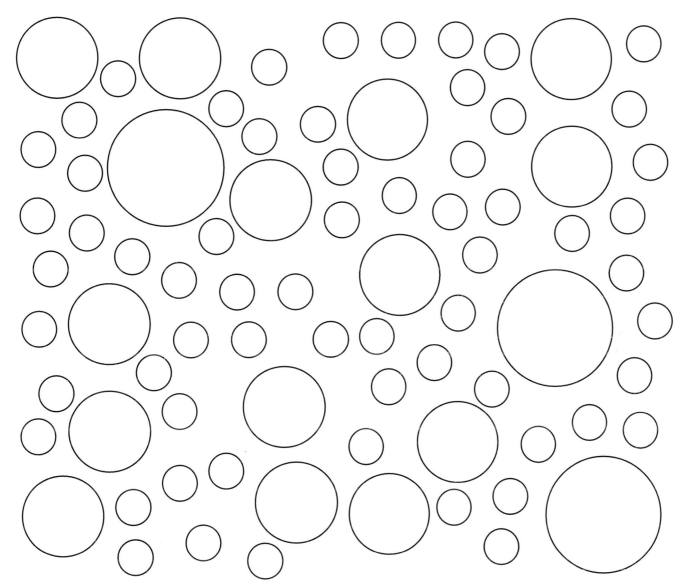

Figure 22: Eighty circles

the average diameter for the circles in his/her random sample. The sample mean diameters for the entire class can be summarized for the two selection procedures with back-to-back stemplots.

How do the means for the two sample selection procedures compare with the true mean diameter of 1.25 cm? Personal selection usually will tend to yield sample means that are larger than 1.25. That is, personal selection tends to be biased with a systematic favoring toward the larger circles and an overestimation of the population mean. Random selection tends to produce some sample means that underestimate the population mean and some that overestimate the population mean, such that the sample means cluster somewhat evenly around the population mean value (i.e., random selection tends to be *unbiased*).

In the previous example, the fact that the sample means vary from one sample to another illustrates an idea that was introduced earlier in the favorite music type survey. This is the notion of sampling variability. Imposing randomness into the sampling procedure allows us to *use probability* to describe the long-run behavior in the variability of the sample means resulting from random sampling. The variation in results from repeated sampling is described through what is called the *sampling distribution*. Sampling distributions will be explored in more depth at Level C.

Comparative Experiments

Another important statistical method that should be introduced at Level B is *comparative experimental studies*. Comparative experimental studies involve comparisons of the effects of two or more *treatments* (experimental conditions) on some response variable. At Level B, studies comparing two treatments are adequate. For example, students might want to study the effects of listening to rock music on one's ability to memorize. Before undertaking a study such as this, it is important for students to have the opportunity to identify and, as much as possible, control for any potential extraneous sources that may interfere with our ability to interpret the results. To address these issues, the class needs to develop a design strategy for collecting appropriate experimental data.

One simple experiment would be to *randomly* divide the class into two equal-sized (or near equal-sized) groups. Random assignment provides a fair way to assign students to the two groups because it tends to average out differences in student ability and other characteristics that might affect the response. For example, suppose a class has 28 students. The 28 students are randomly assigned into two groups of 14. One way to accomplish this is to place 28 pieces of paper in a box—14 labeled "M" and 14 labeled "S." Mix the contents in the box well and have each student randomly choose a piece of paper. The 14 Ms will listen to music and the 14 Ss will have silence.

Table 9: Five-Number Summaries

	Music	Silence
Minimum	3	6
First Quartile	6	8
Median	7	10
Third Quartile	9	12
Maximum	15	14

Each student will be shown a list of words. Rules for how long students have to study the words and how long they have to reproduce the words must be determined. For example, students may have two minutes to study the words, a one-minute pause, and then two minutes to reproduce (write down) as many words as possible. The number of words remembered under each condition (listening to music or silence) is the response variable of interest.

The Five-Number Summaries and comparative boxplots for a hypothetical set of data are shown in Table 9 and Figure 23. These results suggest that students generally memorize fewer words when listening to music than when there is silence. With the exception of the maximum value in the music group (which is classified as an outlier), all summary measures for the music group (labeled M in Figure 23) are lower than the corresponding summary measures for the silence group (labeled S in Figure 23). Without the outlier, the degree of variation in the scores appears to be similar for both groups. Distribution S appears to be reasonably

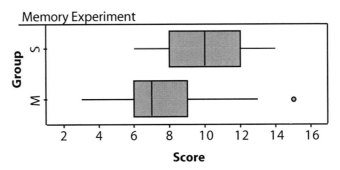

Figure 23: Boxplot for memory data

symmetric, while distribution M is slightly right-skewed. Considering the degree of variation in the scores and the separation in the boxplots, a difference of three between the medians is quite large.

Time Series

Another important statistical tool that should be introduced at Level B is a time series plot. Problems that explore trends in data over time are quite common. For example, the populations of the United States and the world continue to grow, and there are several factors that affect the size of a population, such as the number of births and the number of deaths per year. One question we ask is:

How has the number of live births changed over the past 30 years?

The U.S. Census Bureau publishes vital statistics in its annual *Statistical Abstract of the United States*. The data below are from *The Statistical Abstract of the United States* (2004–2005) and represent the number of live births

Table 10: Live Birth Data

Year	Births (x 1,000)	Year	Births (x 1,000)
1970	3,731	1985	3,761
1971	3,556	1986	3,757
1972	3,258	1987	3,809
1973	3,137	1988	3,910
1974	3,160	1989	4,041
1975	3,144	1990	4,158
1976	3,168	1991	4,111
1977	3,327	1992	4,065
1978	3,333	1993	4,000
1979	3,494	1994	3,979
1980	3,612	1995	3,900
1981	3,629	1996	3,891
1982	3,681	1997	3,881
1983	3,639	1998	3,942
1984	3,669	1999	3,959

per year (in thousands) for residents of the United States since 1970. Note that, in 1970, the value 3,731 represents 3,731,000 live births.

The time series plot in Figure 24 shows the number of live births over time. This graph indicates that:

→ from 1970 to 1975, the number of live births generally declined

→ from 1976 to 1990, the number of live births generally increased

→ from 1991 to 1997, the number of live births generally declined

And it appears that the number of live births may have started to increase since 1997.

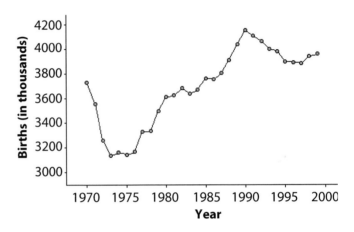

Figure 24: Time series plot of live births

Misuses of Statistics

The introduction of this document points out that data govern our lives. Because of this, every high-school graduate deserves to have a solid foundation in statistical reasoning. Along with identifying proper uses of statistics in questionnaires and graphs, the Level B student should become aware of common misuses of statistics.

Proportional reasoning allows the Level B student to interpret data summarized in a variety of ways. One type of graph that often is misused for representing data is the pictograph. For example, suppose the buying power of a dollar today is 50% of what it was 20 years ago. How would one represent that in a pictograph? Let the buying power of a dollar 20 years ago be represented by the following dollar bill:

If the buying power today is half what it was 20 years ago, one might think of reducing both the width and height of this dollar by one-half, as illustrated in the pictograph below:

Today's dollar at "half" size, representing that it buys only half of what it did 20 years ago.

Today's dollar should look half the size of the dollar of 20 years ago. Does it? Since both the length and the width were cut in half, the area of today's dollar shown above is one-fourth the original area, not one-half.

The two pictographs below show the correct reduction in area. The one on top changes only one dimension, while the other changes both dimensions, but in correct proportion so that the area is one-half the area of the original representation. This example provides the Level B student with an excellent exercise in proportional reasoning.

Today's dollar at half size, with 50% taken from the length.

Today's dollar at half size, with sides in correct proportion to the original.

Poorly designed statistical graphs are commonly found in newspapers and other popular media. Several examples of bad graphs, including the use of an unwarranted third dimension in bar graphs and circle graphs can be found at *www.amstat.org/education/gaise/2*, a web site managed by Carl Schwarz at Simon Fraser University. Students at Level B should be given opportunities to identify graphs that incorrectly represent data and then draw, with the aid of statistical computer

" Poorly designed statistical graphs are commonly found in newspapers and other popular media. "

software, the correct versions. This gives them excellent practice in calculating areas and volumes.

There are many famous misuses of data analysis in the literature, and three are mentioned here. The magazine *Literary Digest* erred in 1936 when it projected that Alf Landon would defeat Franklin Delano Roosevelt by a 57 to 43 percent margin based on responses to its survey. Each survey included a subscription form to the magazine, and more than 2.3 million were returned. Unfortunately, even large voluntary response surveys are generally not representative of the entire population, and Roosevelt won with 62% of the vote. George Gallup correctly projected the winner, and thereby began a very successful career in using random sampling techniques for conducting surveys. Learning what Gallup did right and the *Literary Digest* did wrong gives the Level B student valuable insight into survey design and analysis. A more detailed discussion of this problem can be found in Hollander and Proschan (1984).

The 1970 Draft Lottery provides an example of incorrectly applying randomness. In the procedure that was used, capsules containing birth dates were placed in a large box. Although there was an effort to mix the capsules, it was insufficient to overcome the fact that the capsules were placed in the box in order from January to December. This resulted in young men with birth dates in the latter months being more likely to have their dates selected sooner than birth dates elsewhere in the year. Hollander and Proschan (1984) give an excellent discussion of this problem.

The 25th flight of NASA's space shuttle program took off on January 20, 1986. Just after liftoff, a puff of gray smoke could be seen coming from the right solid rocket booster. Seventy-three seconds into the flight, the *Challenger* exploded, killing all seven astronauts aboard. The cause of the explosion was determined to be an O-ring failure, due to cold weather. The disaster possibly could have been avoided had available data been displayed in a simple scatterplot and correctly interpreted. The *Challenger* disaster has become a case study in the possible catastrophic consequences of poor data analysis.

Summary of Level B

Understanding the statistical concepts of Level B enables a student to begin to appreciate that data analysis is an investigative process consisting of formulating their own questions, collecting appropriate data through various sources (censuses, nonrandom and random sample surveys, and comparative experiments with random assignment), analyzing data through graphs and simple summary measures, and interpreting results with an eye toward inference to a population based on a sample. As they begin to formulate their own questions, students become aware that the world around them is filled with data that affect their own lives, and they begin to appreciate that statistics can help them make decisions based on data. This will help them begin to appreciate that statistics can help them make decisions based on data, investigation, and sound reasoning.

In This Section

→ An Introductory Example—
Obesity in America

→ The Investigatory Process
at Level C

Formulating Questions

**Collecting Data—Types
of Statistical Studies**

Sample Surveys

Experiments

Observational Studies

Analyzing Data

→ Example 1: The Sampling
Distribution of a Sample Proportion

→ Example 2: The Sampling
Distribution of a Sample Mean

Interpreting Results

Generalizing from Samples

Generalizing from Experiments

→ Example 3: A Survey of Music
Preferences

→ Example 4: An Experiment
on the Effects of Light on the
Growth of Radish Seedlings

→ Example 5: Estimating the Density
of the Earth—A Classical Study

→ Example 6: Linear Regression
Analysis—Height vs. Forearm
Length

→ Example 7: Comparing
Mathematics Scores—
An Observational Study

→ Example 8: Observational Study—
Toward Establishing Causation

→ The Role of Probability in Statistics

→ Summary of Level C

Level C is designed to build on the foundation developed in Levels A and B. In particular, Levels A and B introduced students to statistics as an investigatory process, the importance of using data to answer appropriately framed questions, types of variables (categorical versus numerical), graphical displays (including bar graph, dotplot, stemplot, histogram, boxplot, and scatterplot), tabular displays (including two-way frequency tables for categorical data and both ungrouped and grouped frequency/relative frequency tables for numerical data), and numerical summaries (including counts, proportions, mean, median, range, quartiles, interquartile range, MAD, and QCR).

Additionally, Levels A and B covered common study designs (including census, simple random sample, and randomized designs for experiments), the process of drawing conclusions from data, and the role of probability in statistical investigations.

At Level C, all of these ideas are revisited, but the types of studies emphasized are of a deeper statistical nature. Statistical studies at this level require students to draw on basic concepts from earlier work, extend the concepts to cover a wider scope of investigatory issues, and develop a deeper understanding of inferential reasoning and its connection to probability. Students also should have increased ability to explain statistical reasoning to others.

At Level C, students develop additional strategies for producing, interpreting, and analyzing data to help answer questions of interest. In general, students should be able to formulate questions that can be answered with data; devise a reasonable plan for collecting appropriate data through observation, sampling, or experimentation; draw conclusions and use data to support these conclusions; and understand the role random variation plays in the inference process.

Specifically, Level C recommendations include:

I. Formulate Questions

→ Students should be able to formulate questions and determine how data can be collected and analyzed to provide an answer.

II. Collect Data

→ Students should understand what constitutes good practice in conducting a sample survey.

→ Students should understand what constitutes good practice in conducting an experiment.

→ Students should understand what constitutes good practice in conducting an observational study.

→ Students should be able to design and implement a data collection plan for statistical studies, including observational studies, sample surveys, and simple comparative experiments.

III. Analyze Data

→ Students should be able to identify appropriate ways to summarize numerical or categorical data using tables, graphical displays, and numerical summary statistics.

→ Students should understand how sampling distributions (developed through simulation) are used to describe the sample-to-sample variability of sample statistics.

→ Students should be able to recognize association between two categorical variables.

→ Students should be able to recognize when the relationship between two numerical variables is reasonably linear, know that Pearson's correlation coefficient is a measure of the strength of the linear relationship between two numerical variables, and understand the least squares criterion in line fitting.

IV. Interpret Results

→ Students should understand the meaning of statistical significance and the difference between statistical significance and practical significance.

→ Students should understand the role of p-values in determining statistical significance.

→ Students should be able to interpret the margin of error associated with an estimate of a population characteristic.

An Introductory Example–Obesity in America

Data and the stories that surround the data must be of interest to students! It is important to remember this when teaching data analysis. It is also important to choose data and stories that have enough depth to demonstrate the need for statistical thinking. The following example illustrates this.

Students are interested in issues that affect their lives, and issues of health often fall into that category. News items are an excellent place to look for stories of current interest, including items on health. One health-related topic making lots of news lately is obesity. The following paragraph relates to a news story that is rich enough to provide a context for many of the statistical topics to be covered at Level C.

A newspaper article that appeared in 2004 begins with the following lines: "Ask anyone: Americans are getting fatter and fatter. Advertising campaigns say they are. So do federal officials and the scientists they rely on.... In 1991, 23% of Americans fell into the obese category; now 31% do, a more than 30% increase. But Dr. Jeffrey Friedman, an obesity researcher at Rockefeller University, argues that contrary to popular opinion, national data do not show Americans growing uniformly fatter. Instead, he says, the statistics demonstrate clearly that while the very fat are getting fatter, thinner people have remained pretty much the same....The average weight of the population has increased by just seven to 10 pounds." The discussion in the article refers to adults.

The following are suggested questions to explore with students who have a Level B background in statistics, but are moving on to Level C.

→ Sketch a histogram showing what you think a distribution of weights of American adults might have looked like in 1991. Adjust the sketch to show what the distribution of weights might have looked like in 2002, the year of the reported study. Before making your sketches, think about the shape, center, and spread of your distributions. Will the distribution be skewed or symmetric? Will the median be smaller than, larger than, or about the same size as the mean? Will the spread increase as you move from the 1991 distribution to the 2002 distribution?

→ Which sounds more newsworthy: "Obesity has increased by more than 30%" or "On the average, the weight of Americans has increased by fewer than 10 pounds"? Explain your reasoning.

→ The title of the article is *The Fat Epidemic: He Says It's an Illusion.* [See *New York Times*, June 8, 2004, or *CHANCE*, Vol. 17., No. 4, Fall 2004, p. 3 for the complete article.] Do you think this is a fair title? Explain your reasoning.

→ The data on which the percentages are based come from the National Center for Health Statistics, National Health and Nutrition Examination Survey 2002. This is a survey of approximately 5,800 residents of the United States. Although the survey design is more complicated than a simple random sample, the margin of error calculated as if it were a simple random sample is a reasonable approximation. What is an approximate margin of error associated with the 31% estimate of obesity for 2004? Interpret this margin of error for a newspaper reader who never studied statistics.

For the curious, information about how obesity is defined can be found at *www.amstat.org/education/gaise/3*.

In answering these questions, students at Level C should realize that a distribution of weights is going to be skewed toward the larger values. This generally produces a situation in which the mean is larger than the median. Because 8% shifted over the obesity line between 1991 and 2002, but the average weight (or center) did not shift very much, the upper tail of the distribution must have gotten "fatter," indicating a larger spread for the 2002 data. Students will have a variety of interesting answers for the second and third questions. The role of the teacher is to help students understand whether their answers are supported by the facts. The last question gets students thinking about an important estimation concept studied at Level C.

The Investigatory Process at Level C

Because Level C revisits many of the same topics addressed at Levels A and B, but at a deeper and more sophisticated level, we begin by describing how the investigatory process looks at Level C. This general discussion is followed by several examples.

Formulating Questions

As stated at the beginning of Level A, data are more than just numbers. Students need to understand the types of questions that can be answered with data. For example, the question "Is the overall health of high-school students declining in this country?" is too big a question to answer with a statistical investigation (or even many statistical investigations). Certain aspects of the health of students, however, can be investigated by formulating more specific questions, such as "What is the rate of obesity among high-school students?"; "What is the average daily caloric intake for high-school seniors?"; "Is a three-day-a-week exercise regimen enough to maintain heart rate and weight within acceptable limits?" Question formulation, then, becomes the starting point for a statistical investigation.

Collecting Data—Types of Statistical Studies

Most questions that can be answered through data collection and interpretation require data from a designed study, either a *sample survey* or an *experiment*.

These two types of statistical investigations have some common elements—each requires randomization for both purposes of reducing bias and building a foundation for statistical inference and each makes use of the common inference mechanisms of margin of error in estimation and p-value in hypothesis testing (both to be explained later). But these two types of investigations have very different objectives and requirements. Sample surveys are used to estimate or make decisions about characteristics (parameters) of populations. A well-defined, fixed population is the main ingredient of such a study. Experiments are used to estimate or compare the effects of different experimental conditions (treatments), and require well-defined treatments and experimental units on which to study those treatments.

Estimating the proportion of residents of a city that would support an increase in taxes for education requires a sample survey. If the selection of residents is random, then the results from the sample can be extended to represent the population from which the sample was selected. A measure of sampling error (margin of error) can be calculated to ascertain how far the estimate is likely to be from the true value.

Testing to see if a new medication to improve breathing for asthma patients produces greater lung capacity than a standard medication requires an experiment in which a group of patients who have consented to participate in the study are randomly assigned to either the new or the standard medication. With this type of randomized comparative design, an investigator can determine, with a measured degree of uncertainty, whether the new medication caused an improvement in lung capacity. Randomized experiments are, in fact, the only type of statistical study capable of establishing cause and effect relationships. Any generalization extends only to the types of units used in the experiment, however, as the experimental units are not usually randomly sampled from a larger population. To generalize to a larger class of experimental units, more experiments would have to be conducted. That is one reason why replication is a hallmark of good science.

Studies that have no random selection of sampling units or random assignment of treatments to experimental units are called *observational studies* in this document. A study of how many students in your high school have asthma and how this breaks down among gender and age groups would be of this type. Observational studies are not amenable to statistical inference in the usual sense of the term, but they can provide valuable insight into the distribution of measured values and the types of associations among variables that might be expected.

At Level C, students should understand the key features of both sample surveys and experimental designs, including how to set up simple versions of both types of investigations, how to analyze the data appropriately (as the correct analysis is related to the design), and how to clearly and precisely state conclusions for these designed studies. Key elements of the design and implementation of data collection plans for these types of studies follow.

Sample Surveys

Students should understand that obtaining good results from a sample survey depends on four basic features: the population, the sample, the randomization process that connects the two, and the accuracy of the measurements made on the sampled elements. For example, to investigate a question on health of students, a survey might be planned for a high school. What is the population to be investigated? Is it all the students in the school (which changes on a daily basis)? Perhaps the questions of interest involve only juniors and seniors. Once the population is defined as precisely as possible, one must determine an appropriate sample size and a method for randomly selecting a sample of that size. Is there, for example, a list of students who can then be numbered for random selection? Once the sampled students are found, what questions will be asked? Are the questions fair and unbiased (as far as possible)? Can or will the students actually answer them accurately?

When a sample of the population is utilized, errors may occur for several reasons, including:

→   the sampling procedure is biased

→   the sample was selected from the wrong population

> When randomness is incorporated into the sampling procedure, probability provides a way to describe the 'long-run' behavior of sampling variability.

→ some of the units selected to be in the sample were unable (or unwilling) to participate

→ the questions were poorly written

→ the responses were ambiguous

These types of errors should be considered carefully before the study begins so plans can be made to reduce their chance of occurring as much as possible. One way to resolve the bias in the sampling procedure is to incorporate randomness into the selection process.

Two samples of size 50 from the same population of students will most likely not give the same result on, say, the proportion of students who eat a healthy breakfast. This variation from sample to sample is called *sampling variability*. When randomness is incorporated into the sampling procedure, probability provides a way to describe the "long-run" behavior of this sampling variability.

Experiments

At Level C, students should understand that obtaining good results from an experiment depends upon four basic features: well-defined treatments, appropriate experimental units to which these treatments can be assigned, a sound randomization process for assigning treatments to experimental units, and accurate measurements of the results of the experiment. Experimental units generally are not randomly selected from a population of possible units. Rather, they are the ones that happen to be available for the study. In

experiments with human subjects, the people involved are often volunteers who have to sign an agreement stating they are willing to participate in the experimental study. In experiments with agricultural crops, the experimental units are the field plots that happen to be available. In an industrial experiment on process improvement, the units may be the production lines in operation during a given week.

As in a sample survey, replicating an experiment will produce different results. Once again, random assignment of experimental units to treatments (or vice versa) allows the use of probability to predict the behavior in the resulting values of summary statistics from a large number of replications of the experiment. Randomization in experiments is important for another reason. Suppose a researcher decides to assign treatment A only to patients over the age of 60 and treatment B only to patients under the age of 50. If the treatment responses differ, it is impossible to tell whether the difference is due to the treatments or the ages of the patients. (This kind of bias in experiments and other statistical studies is called *confounding*.) The randomization process, if properly done, will usually balance treatment groups so this type of bias is minimized.

Observational Studies

At Level C, students should understand that observational studies are useful for suggesting patterns in data and relationships between variables, but do not provide a strong foundation for estimating population parameters

66

or establishing differences among treatments. Asking the students in one classroom whether they eat a healthy breakfast is not going to help you establish the proportion of healthy breakfast-eaters in the school, as the students in one particular classroom may not be representative of the students in the school. Random sampling is the only way to be confident of a representative sample for statistical purposes. Similarly, feeding your cats Diet A and your neighbor's cats Diet B is not going to allow you to claim that one diet is better than the other in terms of weight control, because there was no random assignment of experimental units (cats) to treatments (diets). As a consequence, confounding may result. Studies of the type suggested above are merely observational; they may suggest patterns and relationships, but they are not a reliable basis for statistical inference.

Analyzing Data

When analyzing data from well-designed sample surveys, students at Level C should understand that an appropriate analysis is one that can lead to justifiable inferential statements about population parameters based on estimates from sample data. The ability to draw conclusions about the population using information from a sample depends on information provided by the sampling distribution of the sample statistic being used to summarize the sample data. At Level C, the two most common parameters of interest are the population proportion for categorical data and the

population mean for numerical data. The appropriate sample statistics used to estimate these parameters are the sample proportion and the sample mean, respectively. At Level C, the sample-to-sample variability, as described by the sampling distribution for each of these two statistics, is addressed in more depth.

Exploring how the information provided by a sampling distribution is used for generalizing from a sample to the larger population enables students at Level C to draw more sophisticated conclusions from statistical studies. At Level C, it is recommended that the sampling distributions of a sample proportion and of a sample mean be developed through simulation. More formal treatment of sampling distributions can be left to AP Statistics and college-level introductory statistics courses.

Because the sampling distribution of a sample statistic is a topic with which many teachers may not be familiar, several examples are included here to show how simulation can be used to obtain an approximate sampling distribution for a sample proportion and for a sample mean.

Example 1: The Sampling Distribution of a Sample Proportion

Properties of the sampling distribution for a sample proportion can be illustrated by simulating the process of selecting a random sample from a population using random digits as a device to model various populations.

For example, suppose a population is assumed to have 60% "successes" ($p = .6$) and we are to take a random sample of $n = 40$ cases from this population. How far can we expect the sample proportion of successes to deviate from the true population value of .60? This can be answered by determining an empirical sampling distribution for the sample proportion.

One way to model a population with 60% successes (and 40% failures) is to utilize the 10 digits 0, 1,…, 9. Label six of the 10 digits as "success" and the other four as "failures." To simulate selecting a sample of size 40 from this population, randomly select 40 random digits (with replacement). Record the number of successes out of the 40 digits selected and convert this count to the proportion of successes in the sample. Note that:

Proportion of Successes in the Sample

$$= \frac{\text{Number of Successes in the Sample}}{\text{Sample Size}}$$

Repeating this process a large number of times, and determining the proportion of successes for each sample, illustrates the idea of the sample-to-sample variability in the sample proportion.

Simulating the selection of 200 random samples of size 40 from a population with 60% successes and determining the proportion of success for each sample

resulted in the empirical distribution shown in Figure 25. This empirical distribution is an approximation to the true sampling distribution of the sample proportion for samples of size 40 from a population in which the actual proportion is .60.

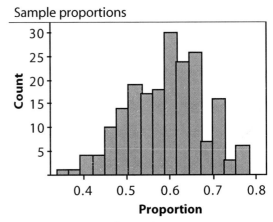

Figure 25: Histogram of sample proportions

Summarizing the above distribution based on its shape, center, and spread, one can state that this empirical sampling distribution has a mound shape (approximately normal). Because the mean and standard deviation of the 200 sample proportions are .59 and .08, respectively, the empirical distribution shown in Figure 25 has a mean of .59 and a standard deviation of .08.

By studying this empirical sampling distribution, and others that can be generated in the same way, students will see patterns emerge. For example, students will observe that, when the sample size is reasonably large (and the population proportion of successes is not too near the extremes of 0 or 1), the shapes of the resulting empirical sampling distributions are approximately normal. Each of the empirical sampling distributions should be centered near the value of p, the population proportion of successes, and the standard deviation for each distribution should be close to:

$$\sqrt{\frac{p(1-p)}{n}}$$

Note that in Example 1, the mean of the empirical distribution is .59, which is close to .6, and the standard deviation is .08, which is close to:

$$\sqrt{\frac{.6(.4)}{40}} \approx .0775$$

A follow-up analysis of these empirical sampling distributions can show students that about 95% of the sample proportions lie within a distance of:

$$2\sqrt{\frac{.6(.4)}{40}} \approx 0.155$$

from the true value of p. This distance is called the *margin of error.*

Example 2: The Sampling Distribution of a Sample Mean

Properties of the sampling distribution for a sample mean can be illustrated in a way similar to that used for proportions in Example 1. Figure 26 shows the distribution of the sample mean when 200 samples of

30 random digits are selected (with replacement) and the sample mean is computed. This simulates sampling from a population that has a uniform distribution with equal numbers of 0s, 1s, 2s,..., 9s. Note that this population of numerical values has a mean, μ, of 4.5 and a standard deviation, σ, of 2.9.

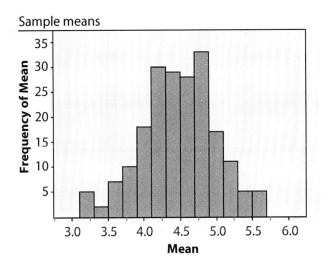

Figure 26: Histogram of sample means

The empirical sampling distribution shown in Figure 26 can be described as approximately normal with a mean of 4.46 (the mean of the 200 sample means from the simulation) and a standard deviation of 0.5 (the standard deviation of the 200 sample means).

By studying this empirical sampling distribution, and others that can be generated in similar ways, students will see patterns emerge. For example, students will observe that, when the sample size is reasonably large, the shapes of the empirical sampling distributions are approximately normal. Each of the empirical sampling distributions should be centered near the value of μ, the population mean, and the standard deviation for each distribution should be close to:

$$\frac{\sigma}{\sqrt{n}}$$

Note that in Example 2, the mean of the empirical sampling distribution is 4.46, which is close to $\mu = 4.5$, and the standard deviation (0.5) is close to:

$$\sigma/\sqrt{n} = 2.9/\sqrt{30} = 0.53$$

The margin of error in estimating a population mean using the sample mean from a single random sample is approximately:

$$2\frac{\sigma}{\sqrt{n}}$$

The sample mean should be within this distance of the true population mean about 95% of the time in repeated random sampling.

Interpreting Results

Generalizing from Samples

The key to statistical inference is the sampling distribution of the sample statistic, which provides information about the population parameter being estimated. As described in the previous section, knowledge of the sampling distribution for a statistic, like a sample proportion or sample mean, leads to a margin of error that provides information about the maximum likely distance between a sample estimate and the population parameter being estimated. Another way to state this key concept of inference is that an estimator plus or minus the margin of error produces an interval of plausible values for the population parameter. Any one of these plausible values could have produced the observed sample result as a reasonably likely outcome.

Generalizing from Experiments

Do the effects of the treatments differ? In analyzing experimental data, this is one of the first questions asked. This question of difference is generally posed in terms of differences between the centers of the data distributions (although it could be posed as a difference between the 90th percentiles or any other measure of location in a distribution). Because the mean is the most commonly used statistic for measuring the center of a distribution, this question of differences is generally posed as a question about a difference in means. The analysis of experimental data, then, usually involves a comparison of means.

Unlike sample surveys, experiments do not depend on random samples from a fixed population. Instead, they require random assignment of treatments to preselected experimental units. The key question, then, is: "Could the observed difference in treatment means be due to the random assignment (chance) alone, or can it be attributed to the treatments administered?"

The following examples are designed to illustrate and further illuminate the important concepts at Level C by carefully considering the four phases of a statistical analysis—question, design, analysis, interpretation—in a variety of contexts.

Example 3: A Survey of Music Preferences

A survey of student music preferences was introduced at Level A, where the analysis consisted of making counts of student responses and displaying the data in a bar graph. At Level B, the analysis was expanded to consider relative frequencies of preferences and cross-classified responses for two types of music displayed in a two-way table. Suppose the survey included the following questions:

1. *What kinds of music do you like?*

    Do you like country music?

    Yes or No

    Do you like rap music?

    Yes or No

    Do you like rock music?

    Yes or No

2. *Which of the following types of music do you like most? Select only one.*

    Country   Rap/Hip Hop   Rock

In order to be able to generalize to all students at the school, a representative sample of students from the school is needed. This could be accomplished by selecting a simple random sample of 50 students from the school. The results can then be generalized to the school (but not beyond), and the Level C discussion will center on basic principles of generalization—or statistical inference.

A Level C analysis begins with a two-way table of counts that summarizes the data on two of the questions: "Do you like rock music?" and "Do you like rap music?" The table provides a way to separately examine the responses to each question and to explore possible connections (association) between the two categorical variables. Suppose the survey of 50 students resulted in the data summarized in Table 11.

As demonstrated at Level B, there are a variety of ways to interpret data summarized in a two-way table, such as Table 11. Some examples based on all 50 students in the survey include:

→   25 of the 50 students (50%) liked both rap and rock music.
→   29 of the 50 students (58%) liked rap music.
→   19 of the 50 students (38%) did not like rock music.

Table 11: Two-Way Frequency Table

		Like Rock Music?		
		Yes	No	Row Totals
Like Rap Music?	Yes	25	4	29
	No	6	15	21
Column Totals		31	19	50

One type of statistical inference relates to conjectures (hypotheses) made before the data were collected. Suppose a student says "I think **more than 50%** of the students in the school like rap music." Because 58% of the students in the sample liked rap music (which is more than 50%), there is evidence to support the student's claim. However, because we have only a sample of 50 students, it is possible that 50% of all students like rap (in which case, the student's claim is not correct), but the variation due to random sampling might produce 58% (or even more) who like rap. The statistical question, then, is whether the sample result of 58% is reasonable from the variation we expect to occur when selecting a random sample from a population with 50% successes.

One way to arrive at an answer is to set up a hypothetical population that has 50% successes (such as even and odd digits produced by a random number generator) and repeatedly take samples of size 50 from it, each time recording the proportion of even digits.

The sampling distribution of proportions so generated will be similar to the one below.

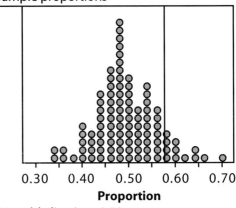

Movable line is at 0.58

Figure 27: Dotplot of sample proportions from a hypothetical population in which 50% like rap music

Based on this simulation, a sample proportion greater than or equal to the observed .58 occurred 12 times out of 100 just by chance variation alone when the actual population proportion is .50. This suggests the result of .58 is not a very unusual occurrence when sampling from a population with .50 as the "true" proportion of students who like rap music. So a population value of .50 is plausible based on what was observed in the sample, and the evidence in support of the student's claim is not very strong. The fraction of times the observed result is matched or exceeded (.12 in this investigation) is called the approximate p-value. The p-value represents the chance of observing the result observed in the sample, or a result more extreme, when the hypothesized value is in fact correct. A small p-value would have supported the student's claim, because this would have indicated that if the population proportion was .50, it would have been very unlikely that a sample proportion of .58 would have been observed.

Suppose another student hypothesized that **more than 40%** of the students in the school like rap music. To test this student's claim, samples of size 50 must now be repeatedly selected from a population that has 40% successes. Figure 28 shows the results of one such simulation. The observed result of .58 was reached only one time out of 100, and no samples produced a proportion greater than .58. Thus, the approximate

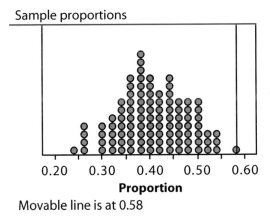

Sample proportions

Movable line is at 0.58

Figure 28: Dotplot of sample proportions from a hypothetical population in which 40% like rap music

p-value is .01, and it is not likely that a population in which 40% of the students like rap music would have produced a sample proportion of 58% in a random sample of size 50. This p-value provides very strong evidence in support of the student's claim that more than 40% of the students in the entire school like rap music.

Another way of stating the above is that .5 is a plausible value for the true population proportion, based on the sample evidence, but .4 is not. A set of plausible values can be found by using the margin of error introduced in Example 1. As explained previously, the margin of error for a sample proportion is approximately:

$$2\sqrt{\frac{p(1-p)}{n}}$$

However, in this problem, the true value of p is unknown. Our sample proportion ($\hat{p} = .58$) is our "best estimate" for what p might be, so the margin of error can be estimated to be:

$$2\sqrt{\frac{\hat{p}(1-\hat{p})}{n}} = 2\sqrt{\frac{.58(.42)}{50}} \approx .14$$

Thus, any proportion between $.58 - .14 = .44$ and $.58 + .14 = .72$ can be considered a plausible value for the true proportion of students at the school who like rap music. Notice that .5 is well within this interval, but .4 is not.

Another type of question that could be asked about the students' music preferences is of the form "Do those who like rock music also tend to like rap music?" In other words, is there an association between liking rock music and liking rap music? The same data from the random sample of 50 students can be used to answer this question.

According to Table 11, a total of 31 students in the survey like rock music. Among those students, the proportion who also like rap music is 25/31 = .81. Among the 19 students who do not like rock music, 4/19 = .21 is the proportion who like rap music. The large difference between these two proportions (.60) suggests there may be a strong association between liking rock music and liking rap music. But could this association simply be due to chance (a consequence only of the random sampling)?

If there were no association between the two groups, then the 31 students who like rock would behave as a random selection from the 50 in the sample. We would expect the proportion who like rap among these 31 students to be close to the proportion who like rap among the 19 students who don't like rock. Essentially, this means that if there is no association, we expect the difference between these two proportions to be approximately 0. Because the difference in our survey is .6, this suggests that there is an association. Can the difference, .6, be explained by the random variation we expect when selecting a random sample?

To simulate this situation, we create a population of 29 1s (those who like rap) and 21 0s (those who do not like rap) and mix them together. Then, we select 31 (representing those who like rock) at random and see how many 1s (those who like rap) we get. It is this entry that goes into the (yes, yes) cell of the table, and from that data the difference in proportions can be calculated. Repeating the process 100 times produces a simulated sampling distribution for the difference between the two proportions, as shown in Figure 29.

Differences between proportions

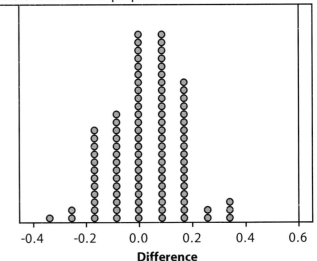

Movable line is at 0.60

Figure 29: Dotplot showing simulated sampling distribution

The observed difference in proportions from the sample data, .6, was never reached in 100 trials, indicating that the observed difference cannot be attributed to chance alone. Thus, there is convincing evidence of a real association between liking rock music and liking rap music.

Example 4: An Experiment on the Effects of Light on the Growth of Radish Seedlings

What is the effect of different durations of light and dark on the growth of radish seedlings? This question was posed to a class of biology students who then set about designing and carrying out an experiment to investigate the question. All possible relative durations of light to dark cannot possibly be investigated in one experiment, so the students decided to focus the question on three treatments: 24 hours of light, 12 hours of light and 12 hours of darkness, and 24 hours of darkness. This covers the extreme cases and one in the middle.

With the help of a teacher, the class decided to use plastic bags as growth chambers. The plastic bags would permit the students to observe and measure the germination of the seeds without disturbing them. Two layers of moist paper towel were put into a disposable plastic bag, with a line stapled about 1/3 of the way from the bottom of the bag (see Figure 30) to hold the paper towel in place and to provide a seam to hold the radish seeds.

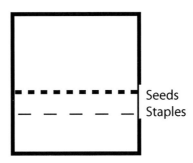

Figure 30: Seed experiment

Although three growth chambers would be sufficient to examine the three treatments, this class made four growth chambers, with one designated for the 24 hours of light treatment, one for the 12 hours of light and 12 hours of darkness treatment, and two for the 24 hours of darkness treatment. One hundred twenty seeds were available for the study. Thirty of the seeds were chosen at random and placed along the stapled seam of the 24 hours of light bag. Thirty seeds were then chosen at random from the remaining 90 seeds and placed in the 12 hours of light and 12 hours of darkness bag. Finally, 30 of the remaining 60 seeds were chosen at random and placed in one of the 24 hours of darkness bags. The final 30 seeds were placed in the other 24 hours of darkness bag. After three days, the lengths of radish seedlings for the germinating seeds were measured and recorded. These data are provided in Table 12; the measurements are in milli-

Table 12: Lengths of Radish Seedlings

Treatment 1 24 light	Treatment 2 12 light, 12 dark	Treatment 3 24 dark		Treatment 1 24 light	Treatment 2 12 light, 12 dark	Treatment 3 24 dark	
2	3	5	20	10	17	15	30
3	4	5	20	10	20	15	30
5	5	8	22	10	20	15	30
5	9	8	24	10	20	15	31
5	10	8	25	10	20	15	33
5	10	8	25	10	20	15	35
5	10	10	25	10	21	16	35
7	10	10	25	10	21	20	35
7	10	10	25	14	22	20	35
7	11	10	26	15	22	20	35
8	13	10	29	15	23	20	35
8	15	11	30	20	25	20	36
8	15	14	30	21	25	20	37
9	15	14	30	21	27	20	38
						20	40

meters. Notice that not all of the seeds in each group germinated.

A good first step in the analyses of numerical data such as these is to make graphs to look for patterns and any unusual departures from the patterns. Boxplots are ideal for comparing data from more than one treatment, as you can see in Figure 31. Both the centers and the spreads increase as the amount of darkness increases. There are three outliers (one at 20 mm and two at 21 mm) in the Treatment 1 (24 hours of light) data. Otherwise, the distributions are fairly symmetric, which is good for statistical inference.

In Figure 31, Treatment 1 is 24 hours of light; treatment 2 is 12 hours of light and 12 of darkness; treatment 3 is 24 hours of darkness.

The summary statistics for these data are shown in Table 13.

Radish seedling lengths

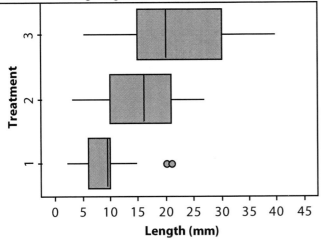

Figure 31: Boxplot showing growth under different conditions

Experiments are designed to compare treatment effects, usually by comparing means. The original question on the effect of different periods of light and dark on the growth of radish seedlings might be turned into two questions about treatment means. Is there evidence that the 12 hours of light and 12 hours of dark (Treatment 2) group has a significantly higher mean than the 24 hours of light (Treatment 1) group? Is there evidence that the 24 hours of dark (Treatment 3) group has a significantly higher mean than the 12 hours of light and 12 hours of dark (Treatment 2) group? Based on the boxplots and the summary statistics, it is clear that the sample means differ. *Are these*

Table 13: Treatment Summary Statistics

Treat-ment	n	Mean	Median	Std. Dev.
1	28	9.64	9.5	5.03
2	28	15.82	16.0	6.76
3	58	21.86	20.0	9.75

differences large enough to rule out chance variation as a possible explanation for the observed difference?

The Treatment 2 mean is 6.2 mm larger than the Treatment 1 mean. If there is no real difference between the two treatments in terms of their effect on seedling growth, then the observed difference must be due to the random assignment of seeds to the bags; that is, one bag was simply lucky enough to get a preponderance of good and lively seeds. But, if a difference this large (6.2 mm) is likely to be the result of randomization alone, then we should see differences of this magnitude quite often if we repeatedly re-randomize the measurements and calculate a new difference in observed means. This, however, is not the case, as one can see from Figure 32. This dotplot was produced by mixing the growth measurements from Treatments 1 and 2 together, randomly splitting them into two groups of 28 measurements, recording the difference in means for the two groups, and repeating the process 200 times.

The observed difference of 6.2 mm was exceeded only one time in 200 trials, for an approximate p-value of

" Experiments are designed to compare treatment effects, usually by comparing means. "

Differences of means

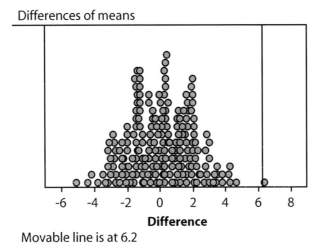

Difference

Movable line is at 6.2

Figure 32: Dotplot showing differences of means

1/200. This is very small, and gives extremely strong evidence to support the hypothesis that there is a statistically significant difference between the means for Treatments 1 and 2. The observed difference of 6.2 mm is very unlikely to be due simply to chance variation.

In a comparison of the means for Treatments 2 and 3, the same procedure is used, except that the combined measurements are split into groups of 28 and 58 each time. The observed difference of 6 mm was exceeded only one time out of 200 trials (see Figure 33), giving extremely strong evidence of a statistically significant difference between the means for Treatments 2 and 3. In summary, the three treatment groups show statistically significant differences in mean growth that cannot reasonably be explained by the random as-

Differences of means

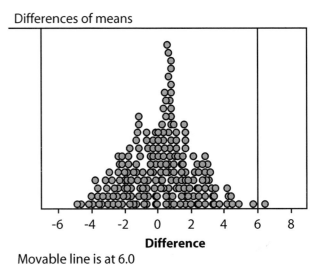

Difference

Movable line is at 6.0

Figure 33: Dotplot showing differences of means

signment of seeds to the bags. This gives us convincing evidence of a treatment effect—the more hours of darkness, the greater the growth of the seedling, at least for these three periods of light versus darkness.

Students should be encouraged to delve more deeply into the interpretation, relating it to what is known about the phenomenon or issue under study. Why do the seedlings grow faster in the dark? Here is an explanation from a biology teacher. It seems to be an adaptation of plants to get the seedlings from the dark (under ground) where they germinate into the light (above ground) as quickly as possible. Obviously, the seedling cannot photosynthesize in the dark and is using up the energy stored in the seed to power the growth. Once the seedling is exposed to light, it shifts its energy away from growing in length to producing chlorophyll and increasing the size of its leaves. These changes allow the plant to become self-sufficient and begin producing its own food. Even though the growth in length of the stem slows, the growth in diameter of the stem increases and the size of the leaves increases. Seedlings that continue to grow in the dark are spindly and yellow, with small yellow leaves. Seedlings grown in the light are a rich, green color with large, thick leaves and short stems.

Example 5: Estimating the Density of the Earth— A Classical Study

What is the density of the Earth? This is a question that intrigued the great scientist Henry Cavendish, who attempted to answer the question in 1798. Cavendish estimated the density of the Earth by using the crude tools available to him at the time. He did not literally take a random sample; he measured on different days and at different times, as he was able. But the density of the Earth does not change over time, so his measurements can be thought of as a random sample of all the measurements he could have taken on this constant. The variation in the measurements is due to his measurement error, not to changes in the Earth's density. The Earth's density is the constant that is being estimated.

This is a typical example of an estimation problem that occurs in science. There is no real "population" of measurements that can be sampled; rather, the sample data is assumed to be a random selection from the conceptual population of all measurements that could have been made. At this point, there may be some confusion between an "experiment" and a "sample survey" because Cavendish actually conducted a scientific investigation to get his measurements. The key, however, is that he conducted essentially the same investigation many times with a goal of estimating a constant, much like interviewing many people to estimate the proportion who favor a certain candidate for office. He did not randomly assign treatments to experimental units for the purpose of comparing treatment effects.

The famous Cavendish data set contains his 29 measurements of the density of the Earth, in grams per cubic centimeter. The data are shown below [Source: *http://lib.stat.cmu.edu/DASL*]:

5.50	5.57	5.42	5.61	5.53	5.47	4.88
5.62	5.63	4.07	5.29	5.34	5.26	5.44
5.46	5.55	5.34	5.30	5.36	5.79	5.75
5.29	5.10	5.86	5.58	5.27	5.85	5.65
5.39						

One should look at the data before proceeding with an analysis. The histogram in Figure 34 shows the data to be roughly symmetric, with one unusually small value. If Cavendish were alive, you could ask him if he had

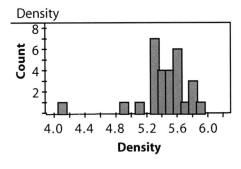

Density

Figure 34: Histogram of Earth density measurements

made a mistake (and that is certainly what you should do for a current data set).

The mean of the 29 measurements is 5.42 and the standard deviation is 0.339. Recall that the margin of error for the sample mean is:

$$2\frac{\sigma}{\sqrt{n}}$$

where σ is the population standard deviation. In this problem, the population standard deviation is not known; however, the sample standard deviation provides an estimate for the population standard deviation. Consequently, the margin of error can be estimated to be:

$$2\frac{s}{\sqrt{n}} = 2\frac{0.339}{\sqrt{29}} = 0.126$$

The analysis shows that any value between 5.420 − 0.126 and 5.420 + 0.126, or in the interval (5.294, 5.546), is a plausible value of the density of the Earth. That is, any value in the interval is consistent with the data obtained by Cavendish. Now, the questionable low observation should be taken into account, as it will lower the mean and increase the standard deviation. If that measurement is regarded as a mistake and removed from the data set, the mean of the 28 remaining observations is 5.468 and the standard deviation is 0.222, producing a margin of error of 0.084 and an interval of plausible values of (5.384, 5.552).

Students now can check on how well Cavendish did; modern methods pretty much agree that the average density of the Earth is about 5.515 grams per cubic centimeter. The great 18th century scientist did well!

Example 6: Linear Regression Analysis—Height vs. Forearm Length

Regression analysis refers to the study of relationships between variables. If the "cloud" of points in a scatterplot of paired numerical data has a linear shape, a straight line may be a realistic model of the relationship between the variables under study. The least squares line runs through the center (in some sense) of the cloud of points. Residuals are defined to be the deviations in the y direction between the points in the scatterplot and the least squares line; spread is now the variation around the least squares line, as

> " Regression analysis refers to the study of relationships between variables. "

Table 14: Heights vs. Forearm Lengths

Forearm (cm)	Height (cm)	Forearm (cm)	Height (cm)
45.0	180.0	41.0	163.0
44.5	173.2	39.5	155.0
39.5	155.0	43.5	166.0
43.9	168.0	41.0	158.0
47.0	170.0	42.0	165.0
49.1	185.2	45.5	167.0
48.0	181.1	46.0	162.0
47.9	181.9	42.0	161.0
40.6	156.8	46.0	181.0
45.5	171.0	45.6	156.0
46.5	175.5	43.9	172.0
43.0	158.5	44.1	167.0

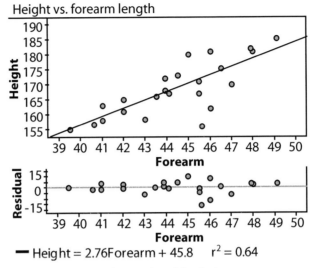

Height = 2.76Forearm + 45.8 $r^2 = 0.64$

Figure 35: Scatterplot and residual plot

measured by the standard deviation of the residuals. When using a fitted model to predict a value of y from x, the associated margin of error depends on the standard deviation of the residuals.

Relationships among various physical features, such as height versus arm span and neck size versus shoe size, can be the basis of many interesting questions for student investigation. If I were painting a picture of a person, how could I get the relative sizes of the body parts correct? This question prompted students to carry out an investigation of one of the possible relationships, that between forearm length and height.

The students responsible for the study sampled other students on which to make forearm and height measurements. Although the details of how the sample actually was selected are not clear, we will suppose that it is representative of students at the school and has the characteristics of a random sample. An important consideration here is to agree on the definition of "forearm" before beginning to take measurements. The data obtained by the students (in centimeters) are provided in Table 14.

A good first step in any analysis is to plot the data, as we have done in Figure 35. The linear trend in the plot is fairly strong. The scatterplot, together with Pearson's correlation coefficient of .8, indicate that a line would be a reasonable model for summarizing the relationship between height and forearm length.

The scatterplot includes a graph of the least squares line:

Predicted Height = 45.8 + 2.76(Forearm Length).

The plot below the scatterplot shows the residuals. There are a few large residuals but no unusual pattern in the residual plot. The slope (about 2.8) can be interpreted as an estimate of the average difference in heights for two persons whose forearms are 1 cm different in length. The intercept of 45.8 centimeters cannot be interpreted as the expected height of a person with a forearm zero centimeters long! However, the regression line can reasonably be used to predict the height of a person for whom the forearm length is known, as long as the known forearm length is in the range of the data used to develop the prediction equation (39 to 50 cm for these data). The margin of error for this type of prediction is approximately 2(standard deviation of the residuals). For these data, the standard deviation of the residuals is 5.8 (not shown here, but provided as part of the computer output), so the margin of error is 2(5.8) = 11.6 cm. The predicted height of someone with a forearm length of 42 cm would be:

Predicted Height = 45.8 + 2.76(42) = 161.7 cm

With 95% confidence, we would predict the height of people with forearm length 42 cm to be between 150.1 cm and 173.3 cm (161.7 ± 11.6).

Is the slope of 2.8 "real," or simply a result of chance variation from the random selection process? This question can be investigated using simulation. A description of this simulation is included in the Appendix to Level C.

Example 7: Comparing Mathematics Scores—An Observational Study

Data often are presented to us in a form that does not call for much analysis, but does require some insight into statistical principles for correct interpretation. Standardized test scores often fall into this category. Table 15 gives information about the state mean scores on the National Assessment of Educational Progress (NAEP) 2000 Grade 4 mathematics scores for Louisiana and Kentucky. Even though these scores are based on a sample of students, these are the scores assigned to the states, and consequently, they can be considered observational data from that point of view.

Table 15: NAEP 2000 Scores in Mathematics

	Overall Mean	Mean for Whites	Mean for Non-whites	% White
Louisiana	217.96	229.51	204.94	
Kentucky	220.99	224.17		87

To see if students understand the table, it is informative to ask them to fill in a few omitted entries.

→ Fill in the two missing entries in the table (53% and 199.71).

More substantive questions involve the seeming contradictions that may occur in data of this type. They might be phrased as follows.

→ For the two states, compare the overall means. Compare the means for whites. Compare the means for nonwhites. What do you observe?

→ Explain why the reversals in direction take place once the means are separated into racial groups.

It is genuinely surprising to students that data summaries (means in this case) can go in one direction in the aggregate but can go in the opposite direction for each subcategory when disaggregated. This phenomenon is called Simpson's Paradox.

Example 8: Observational Study—Toward Establishing Causation

Observational studies are the only option for situations in which it is impossible or unethical to randomly assign treatments to subjects. Such situations are a common occurrence in the study of causes of diseases. A classical example from this field is the relationship between smoking and lung cancer, which prompted heated debates during the 1950s and 1960s. Society will not condone the notion of assigning some people to be smokers and others to be nonsmokers in an experiment to see if smoking causes lung cancer. So the evidence has to be gathered from observing the

Table 16: Cigarette Smoking and Lung Cancer

	Lung Cancer Cases	Controls	Totals
Smokers	647	622	1,269
Non-smokers	2	27	29

world as it is. The data collection process still can be designed in clever ways to obtain as much information as possible.

Here is an example from the smoking versus lung cancer debates. A group of 649 men with lung cancer was identified from a certain population in England. A control group of the same size was established by matching these patients with other men from the same population who did not have lung cancer. The matching was on background variables such as ethnicity, age, and socioeconomic status. (This is called a case-control study.) The objective, then, is to compare the rate of smoking among those with lung cancer to the rate for those without cancer.

First, make sure students understand the nature of the data in Table 16. Does this show, for example, that there was a very high percentage of smokers in England around 1950? The rate of smoking in these groups was $(647/649) = .997$ for the cancer patients and $(622/649) = .958$ for the controls. If these data had resulted from a random assignment or selection, the difference of about 4 percentage points would be statistically significant (by methods discussed earlier), which gives the researcher reason to suspect there is an association here that cannot be attributed to chance alone. Another way to look at these data is to think about randomly selecting one person from among the smokers and one person from among the nonmokers. The smoker has a chance of 647/1269 = .51 of being in the lung cancer column, while the nonsmoker has only a 2/29 = .07 chance of being there. This is evidence of strong association between smoking and lung cancer, but it is not conclusive evidence that smoking is, in fact, the cause of the lung cancer. (This is a good place to have students speculate about other possible causes that could have resulted in data like these.)

Another step in establishing association in observational studies is to see if the increase in exposure to the risk factor produces an increase in incidence of the disease. This was done with the same case-control study by looking at the level of smoking for each person, producing Table 17.

Table 17: Level of Cigarette Smoking and Lung Cancer

Cigarettes/ Day	Lung Cancer Cases	Controls	Probability
0	2	27	0.07
1–14	283	346	0.45
15–24	196	190	0.51
25+	168	84	0.67

The term "probability" is used in the same sense as above. If a person is randomly selected from the 1–14 level, the chance that the person falls into the cancer column is .45, and so on for the other rows. The important result is that these "probabilities" increase with the level of smoking. This is evidence that an increase in the disease rate is associated with an increase in cigarette smoking.

Even with this additional evidence, students should understand that a cause and effect relationship cannot be established from an observational study. The main reason for this is that these observational studies are subject to bias in the selection of patients and controls. Another study of this type could have produced a different result. (As it turned out, many studies of this type produced remarkably similar results. That, coupled with laboratory experiments on animals that established a biological link between smoking and lung cancer, eventually settled the issue for most people.)

The Appendix to Level C contains more examples of the types discussed in this section.

The Role of Probability in Statistics

Teachers and students must understand that statistics and probability are not the same. Statistics uses probability, much as physics uses calculus, but only certain aspects of probability make their way into statistics. The concepts of probability needed for introductory statistics (with emphasis on data analysis) include relative frequency interpretations of data, probability distributions as models of populations of measurements, an introduction to the normal distribution as a model for sampling distributions, and the basic ideas of expected value and random variation. Counting rules, most specialized distributions and the development of theorems on the mathematics of probability should be left to areas of discrete mathematics and/or calculus.

Understanding the reasoning of statistical inference requires a basic understanding of some important ideas in probability. Students should be able to:

→ Understand probability as a long-run relative frequency;

→ Understand the concept of independence; and

→ Understand how probability can be used in making decisions and drawing conclusions.

In addition, because so many of the standard inferential procedures are based on the normal distribution, students should be able to evaluate probabilities using the normal distribution (preferably with the aid of technology).

Probability is an attempt to quantify uncertainty. The fact that the long-run behavior of a random process is predictable leads to the long-run relative frequency interpretation of probability. Students should be able to interpret the probability of an outcome as the long-run proportion of the time the outcome should occur if the random experiment is repeated a large number of times. This long-run relative frequency interpretation of probability also provides the justification for using simulation to estimate probabilities. After observing a large number of chance outcomes, the observed proportion of occurrence for the outcome of interest can be used as an estimate of the relevant probability.

Students also need to understand the concept of independence. Two outcomes are independent if our assessment of the chance that one outcome occurs is not affected by knowledge that the other outcome has occurred. Particularly important to statistical inference is the notion of independence in sampling settings. Random selection (with replacement) from a population ensures the observations in a sample are independent. For example, knowing the value of the third observation does not provide any information about the value of the fifth (or any other) observation. Many of the methods used to draw conclusions about a population based on data from a sample require the observations in a sample to be independent.

Most importantly, the concepts of probability play a critical role in developing statistical methods that make it possible to make inferences based on sample data and to assess our confidence in such conclusions.

To clarify the connection between data analysis and probability, we will return to the key ideas presented in the inference section. Suppose an opinion poll shows 60% of sampled voters in favor of a proposed new law. A basic statistical question is, "How far

> " Probability is an attempt to quantify uncertainty. "

might this sample proportion be from the true population proportion?" That the difference between the estimate and the truth is less than the margin of error approximately 95% of the time is based on a probabilistic understanding of the sampling distribution of sample proportions. For large random samples, this relative frequency distribution of sample proportions is approximately normal. Thus, students should be familiar with how to use appropriate technology to find areas under the normal curve.

Suppose an experimenter divides subjects into two groups, with one group receiving a new treatment for a disease and the other receiving a placebo. If the treatment group does better than the placebo group, a basic statistical question is, "Could the difference have been a result of chance variation alone?" The randomization allows us to determine the probability of a difference being greater than that observed under the assumption of no treatment effect. In turn, this probability allows us to draw a meaningful conclusion from the data. (A proposed model is rejected as implausible, not primarily because the probability of an observed outcome is small, but rather because it is in the tail of a distribution.) An adequate answer to the above question also requires knowledge of the context in which the question was asked and a sound experimental design. This reliance on context and design is one of the basic differences between statistics and mathematics.

As demonstrated earlier, the sampling distribution of a sample mean will be approximately normal under random sampling, as long as the sample size is reasonably large. The mean and standard deviation of this distribution usually are unknown (introducing the need for inference), but sometimes these parameter values can be determined from basic information about the population being sampled. To compute these parameter values, students will need some knowledge of *expected values*, as demonstrated next.

According to the March 2000 Current Population Survey of the U.S. Census Bureau, the distribution of family size is as given by Table 18. (A family is defined as two or more related people living together. The number "7" really is the category "7 or more," but very few families are larger than 7.)

Table 18: Family Size Distribution

Family Size, x	Proportion, p(x)
2	0.437
3	0.223
4	0.201
5	0.091
6	0.031
7	0.017

Notice first the connection between data and probability: These proportions (really estimates from a very large sample survey) can be taken as approximate probabilities for the next survey. In other words, if someone randomly selects a U.S. family for a new survey, the probability that it will have three members is about .223.

Second, note that we now can find the mean and standard deviation of a random variable (call it X), defined as the number of people in a randomly selected family. The mean, sometimes called the *expected value* of X and denoted by E(X), is found using the formula:

$$E(X) = \sum_{\substack{all\ possible \\ x\ values}} x \cdot p(x)$$

which turns out to be 3.11 for this distribution. If the next survey contains 100 randomly selected families, then the survey is expected to produce 3.11 members per family, on the average, for an estimated total of 311 people in the 100 families altogether.

The standard deviation of X, SD(X), is the square root of the variance of X, V(X), given by:

$$V(X) = \sum_{\substack{all\ possible \\ x\ values}} [x - E(X)]^2 \cdot p(x)$$

For the family size data, V(X) = 1.54 and SD(X) = 1.24.

Third, these facts can be assembled to describe the expected sampling distribution of the mean family size in a random sample of 100 families yet to be taken. That sampling distribution will be approximately normal in shape, centering at 3.11 with a standard deviation of $1.24/\sqrt{100} = 0.124$. This would be useful information for the person designing the next survey.

In short, the relative frequency definition of probability, the normal distribution, and the concept of expected value are the keys to understanding sampling distributions and statistical inference.

Summary of Level C

Students at Level C should become adept at using statistical tools as a natural part of the investigative process. Once an appropriate plan for collecting data has been implemented and the resulting data are in hand, the next step usually is to summarize the data using graphical displays and numerical summaries. At Level C, students should be able to select summary techniques appropriate for the type of data available, produce these summaries, and describe in context the important characteristics of the data. Students will use the graphical and numerical summaries learned at Levels A and B, but should be able to provide a more sophisticated interpretation that integrates the context and objectives of the study.

At Level C, students also should be able to draw conclusions from data and support these conclusions using statistical evidence. Students should see statistics as providing powerful tools that enable them to answer questions and to make informed decisions. Students also should understand the limitations of conclusions based on data from sample surveys and experiments, and should be able to quantify uncertainty associated with these conclusions using margin of error and related properties of sampling distributions.

What Are Common Name Lengths?

Formulate Questions

During the first week of school, a third-grade teacher is trying to help her students learn one another's names by playing various games. During one of the games, a student named MacKenzie noticed she and her classmate Zacharius each have nine letters in their names. MacKenzie conjectured that their names were longer than everyone else's names. The teacher decided that this observation by the student provided an excellent opening for a statistics lesson.

The next school day, the teacher reminds students of MacKenzie's comment from the day before and asks the class what they would like to know about their classmates' names. The class generates a list of questions, which the teacher records on the board as follows:

→   Who has the longest name? The shortest?

→   Are there more nine-letter names or six-letter names? How many more?

→   What's the most common name length?

→   How many letters are in all of our names?

→   If you put all of the eight- and nine-letter names together, will there be as many as the five-letter names?

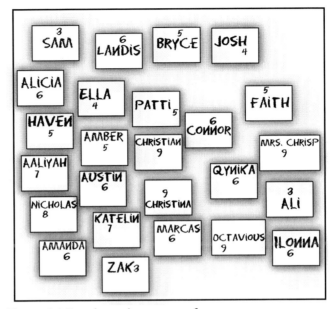

Figure 36: Random placement of names

Collect Data

The statistics lesson begins with students writing their names on sticky notes and posting them on the white board at the front of the room. This is a census of the classroom because they are gathering data from all students in the class.

Given no direction about how to organize the notes, the students arbitrarily place them on the board.

In order to help students think about how to use graphical tools to analyze data, the teacher asks the students if they are easily able to answer any of the

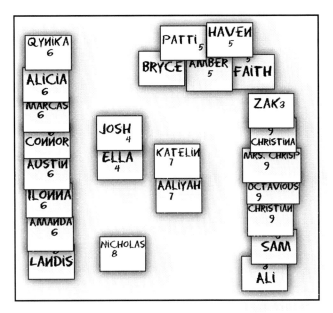

Figure 37: Names clustered by length

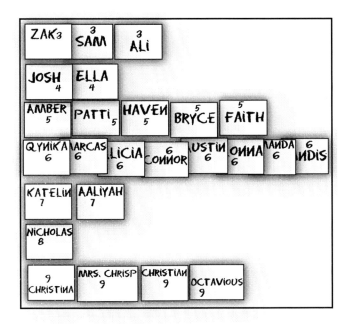

Figure 38: Preliminary dotplot

posed questions now by looking at the sticky notes, and the students say they cannot. The teacher then suggests that they think of ways to better organize the notes. A student suggests grouping the names according to how many letters are in each name.

The teacher again asks if they can easily answer the questions that are posed. The students say they can answer *some* of the questions, but not easily. The teacher asks what they can do to make it easier to answer the questions. Because the students have been constructing graphs since kindergarten, they readily an-

swer, "Make a graph!" The teacher then facilitates a discussion of what kind of graph they will make, and the class decides on a dotplot, given the fact that their names are already on sticky notes and given the available space on the board. Note that this display is *not* a bar graph because bar graphs are made when the data represent a categorical variable (such as favorite color). A dotplot is appropriate for a numerical variable, such as the number of letters in a name.

The teacher then uses computer software to translate this information into a more abstract dotplot, as shown in Figure 39. This helps the students focus on the general shape of the data, rather than on the particular names of the students.

Interpret Results

The teacher then facilitates a discussion of each question posed by the students, using the data displayed in the graph to answer the questions. Students also add appropriate labels and titles to the graph. The teacher helps students use the word "mode" to answer the question about the most common name length. She introduces the term "range" to help students answer the questions about shortest and longest names. Students visualize from the dotplot that there is variability in name length from individual to individual. The range gives a sense of the amount of variability in name length within the class. Using the range, we know that if the name for any two students are compared, the name lengths cannot differ by more than the value for the range.

The teacher then tells the students that there is another useful question they can answer from this data. Sometimes it is helpful to know "about how long most names are." For instance, if you were making place cards for a class lunch party, you might want to know how long the typical name is in order to decide which size of place cards to buy. The typical or average name length is called the mean. Another way to think of this is, "If all of our names were the same length, how long would they be?" To illustrate this new idea, the teach-

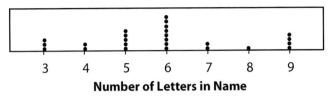

Number of Letters in Name

Figure 39: Computer-generated dotplot

er has students work in groups of four, and each child takes a number of snap cubes equal to the number of letters in his/her name. Then all four children at one table put all of their snap cubes in a pile in the middle of the table. They count how many cubes they have in total. Then they share the cubes fairly, with each child taking one at a time until they are all gone or there are not enough left to share. They record how many cubes each child received. (Students at some tables are able to use fractions to show that, for example, when there are two cubes left, each person could get half a cube. At other tables, the students simply leave the remaining two cubes undistributed.) The teacher then helps the students symbolize what they have done by using addition to reflect putting all the cubes in the middle of the table and using division to reflect sharing the cubes fairly among everyone at the table. They attach the words "mean" and "average" to this idea.

Finally, the students are asked to transfer the data from the sticky notes on the board to their own graphs. The class helps the teacher generate additional questions about the data that can be answered for homework. Because the students' graphs look different, the next

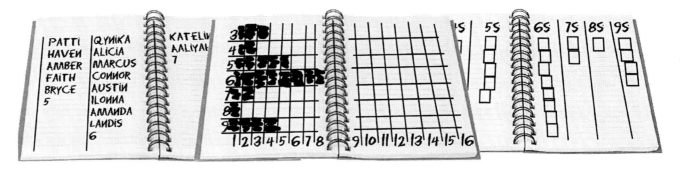

Figure 40: Student-drawn graphs

day the teacher will lead a discussion about the features of the various graphs the students have constructed and the pros and cons of each.

Valentine's Day and Candy Hearts

Formulate Questions

As Valentine's Day approaches, a teacher decides to plan a lesson in which children will analyze the characteristics of a bag of candy hearts. To begin the lesson, the teacher holds up a large bag of candy hearts and asks the children what they know about them from prior experience. The children know that the hearts are different colors and that they have words on them. The teacher asks the children what they wonder about the bag of hearts she is holding. The children want to know how many hearts are in the bag, what they say, and whether there are a lot of pink hearts, because most people like pink ones the best. The teacher tells

the children that they will be able to answer some of those questions about their own bags of candy.

Collect Data

Each child receives a small packet of candy hearts. Students are asked how they can sort their hearts, and the students suggest sorting them by color—a categorical variable. The teacher asks students what question this will help them answer, and the students readily recognize that this will tell them which color candy appears most often in the bag.

Analyze Data

After sorting the candies into piles and counting and recording the number of candies in each pile, the teacher guides the students to make a bar graph with their candies on a blank sheet of paper. The children construct individual bar graphs by lining up all of their pink candies, all of their white candies, etc. The

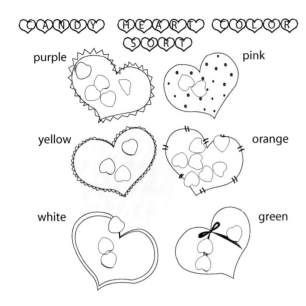

Figure 41: Initial sorting of candies

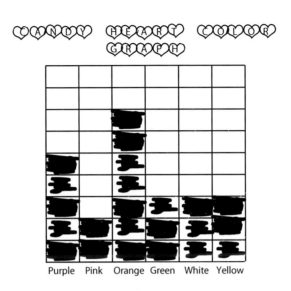

Figure 42: Bar graph of candy color

teacher then provides a grid with color labels on the x-axis and numerical labels on the y-axis so the students can transfer their data from the actual candies to a more permanent bar graph.

Interpret Results

After students construct their individual graphs, the teacher distributes a recording sheet on which each student records what color occurred the most frequently (the modal category) and how many of each color they had. This is followed by a class discussion in which the teacher highlights issues of variability. First,

the students recognize that the number of each color varies within a package. Students also recognize that their packets of candy are not identical, noting that some students had no green hearts while others had no purple hearts. Some students had more pink hearts than any other color, while other students had more white hearts. At Level A, students are acknowledging variability between packages—the concept of between group variability that will be explored in more detail at Level B. The students hypothesize that these variations in packages were due to how the candies were packed by machines. The students also noted differences in the total number of candies per packet, but found this difference to be small. The student with the fewest candies had 12, while the student with the greatest number of candies had 15. The teacher asked students if they had ever read the phrase "packed by weight, not by volume" on the side of a package. The class then discussed what this meant and how it might relate to the number of candies in a bag.

(Note: Images in this example were adapted from *www.littlegiraffes.com/valentines.html*.)

Appendix for Level B

Many questionnaires ask for a "Yes" or "No" response. For example, in the Level B document, we explored connections between whether students like rap music and whether they like rock music. To investigate possible connections between these two categorical variables, the data were summarized in the following *two-way frequency table*, or *contingency table*.

Table 4: Two-Way Frequency Table

		Like Rap Music?		
		Yes	No	**Row Totals**
Like Rock Music?	Yes	27	6	33
	No	4	17	21
Column Totals		31	23	54

Since 82% (27/33) of the students who like rock music also like rap music, students who like rock music tend to like rap music as well. Because students who like rock music tend to like rap music, there is an *association* between liking rock music and liking rap music.

At Level B, we explored the association between height and arm span by examining the data in a scatterplot, and we measured the strength of the association with the Quadrant Count Ratio, or QCR. For the height/arm span problem, both variables are numerical. It also is possible to measure the strength and direction of association between certain types of categorical variables. Recall that two numerical variables are positively associated when above-average values of one variable tend to occur with above-average values of the other and when below-average values of one variable tend to occur with below-average values of the other. Two numerical variables are negatively associated when below-average values of one variable tend to occur with above-average values of the other and when above-average values of one variable tend to occur with below-average values of the other.

The scatterplot below for the height/arm span data includes a vertical line ($x = 172.8$) drawn through the mean height and a horizontal line ($y = 169.3$) drawn through the mean arm span.

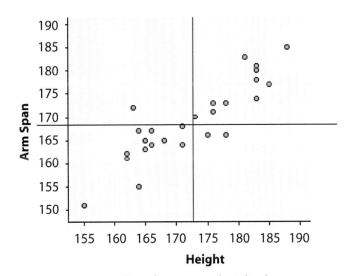

Figure 43: Scatterplot of arm span/height data

An alternative way to summarize the data would have been to ask each student the following two questions:

Is your height above average?

Is your arm span above average?

Note that for these data, the response to each question is either "Yes" or "No."

The 12 individuals in the scatterplot with below-average height and below-average arm span (Quadrant 3) responded "No" to both questions. Because their responses to both questions are the same, these 12 responses are in *agreement*. The 11 individuals in the scatterplot with above-average height and above-average arm span (Quadrant 1) responded "Yes" to both questions. Since their responses to both questions are the same, these 11 responses are in agreement. When the responses to two "Yes/No" questions are the same (No/No) or (Yes/Yes), the responses are in agreement.

The one individual with below-average height and above-average arm span (Quadrant 2) responded "No" to the first question and "Yes" to the second question, (No/Yes). Since her/his responses to the two questions are different, these two responses are in *disagreement*. The two individuals with above-average height and below-average arm span (Quadrant 4) responded "Yes" to the first question and "No" to the second question (Yes/No). Since their responses to the two questions are different, their responses are

in disagreement. When the responses to two "Yes/No" questions are different (No/Yes) or (Yes/No), the responses are in disagreement.

For the data in the scatterplot in Figure 43, the results to the above two questions can be summarized in the following 2x2 two-way frequency table:

Table 19: 2x2 Two-Way Frequency Table

		Height above Average?		Row Totals
		No	Yes	
Arm Span above Average?	No	12	2	14
	Yes	1	11	12
Column Totals		13	13	26

Notice that there are a total of 23 responses in agreement (12 No/No and 11 Yes/Yes to the height/arm span questions), and that these correspond to the points in Quadrants 3 and 1, respectively, in the scatterplot. Also, there are a total of three responses in disagreement (two Yes/No and one No/Yes), and these correspond to the points in Quadrants 4 and 2, respectively. Recall that the QCR is determined as follows:

$$\frac{(\text{Number of Points in Quadrants 1 and 3}) - (\text{Number of Points in Quadrants 2 and 4})}{\text{Number of Points in all Four Quadrants}}$$

Restated in terms of Table 19:

$$QCR = \frac{\begin{array}{c}\text{(Number of Points in Agreement)} \\ - \text{(Number of Points in Disagreement)}\end{array}}{\text{Number of Points in all Four Quadrants}}$$

Based on this, we can say that two "Yes/No" categorical variables are positively associated when the responses tend to be in agreement—the more observations in agreement, the stronger the positive association. Negative association between two "Yes/No" categorical variables occurs when the responses tend to be in disagreement—the more observations in disagreement, the stronger the negative association.

The responses to two "Yes/No" questions can be summarized as follows in a two-way frequency table:

Table 20: Two-Way Frequency Table

		Question 1		Row Totals
		No	Yes	
Question 2	No	a	b	$r_1 = a+b$
	Yes	c	d	$r_2 = c+d$
Column Totals		$c_1 = a+c$	$c_2 = b+d$	$T = a+b+c+d$

Note: a = the number who respond No/No; b = the number who respond Yes/No; c = the number who respond No/Yes; d = the number who respond Yes/Yes.

Conover (1999) suggests the following measure of association based on a 2x2 table summarized as above.

$$\frac{(a+d) - (b+c)}{T}$$

Let's call this measure the *Agreement-Disagreement Ratio* (ADR). Note that this measure of association is analogous to the QCR correlation coefficient for two numerical variables.

The ADR for the height/arm span data is:

$$ADR = \frac{(12+11) - (2+1)}{26} = .77$$

An ADR of .77 indicates a strong positive association between height and arm span measurements.

Recall the music example data, which were summarized as follows:

Table 21: Two-Way Frequency Table

		Like Rap Music?		Row Totals
		No	Yes	
Like Rock Music?	No	17	4	21
	Yes	6	27	33
Column Totals		23	31	54

The ADR for the rap/rock data is:

$$ADR = \frac{(17 + 27) - (4+6)}{54} = .63$$

An ADR of .63 indicates a fairly strong association between liking rock and liking rap music.

Another question presented in Level B was:

Do students who like country music tend to like or dislike rap music?

Data collected on 54 students are summarized in the following two-way frequency table:

Table 22: Two-Way Frequency Table

		Like Rap Music?		
		No	Yes	**Row Totals**
Like Country Music?	No	10	22	32
	Yes	13	9	22
Column Totals		23	31	54

For these data,

$$\text{ADR} = \frac{(10+9) - (22+13)}{54} = -.30$$

An ADR of –.30 indicates a negative association between liking country music and liking rap music.

The QCR and the ADR are additive in nature, in that they are based on "how many" data values are in each quadrant or cell. Conover (1999) suggests the *phi coefficient* as another possible measure of association for data summarized in a 2x2 table.

$$\text{Phi} = \frac{ad - bc}{\sqrt{r_1 r_2 c_1 c_2}}$$

Conover points out that Phi is analogous to Pearson's correlation coefficient for numerical data. Both Phi and Pearson's correlation coefficient are multiplicative, and Pearson's correlation coefficient is based on "how far" the points in each quadrant are from the center point.

Recall that in Example 6 of Level C, students investigated the relationship between height and forearm length. The observed data are shown again here as Table 14, and the resulting plots and regression analysis are given in Figure 35.

Regression Analysis: Height versus Forearm

The regression equation is:

Predicted Height = 45.8 + 2.76 (Forearm)

Table 14: Heights vs. Forearm Lengths

Forearm (cm)	Height (cm)	Forearm (cm)	Height (cm)
45.0	180.0	41.0	163.0
44.5	173.2	39.5	155.0
39.5	155.0	43.5	166.0
43.9	168.0	41.0	158.0
47.0	170.0	42.0	165.0
49.1	185.2	45.5	167.0
48.0	181.1	46.0	162.0
47.9	181.9	42.0	161.0
40.6	156.8	46.0	181.0
45.5	171.0	45.6	156.0
46.5	175.5	43.9	172.0
43.0	158.5	44.1	167.0

Is the slope of 2.8 "real," or simply a result of the chance variation from the random selection

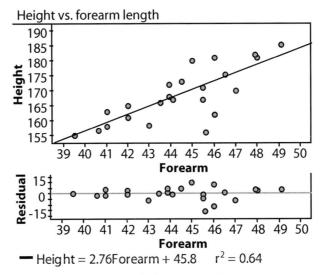

Height vs. forearm length

Height = 2.76Forearm + 45.8 $r^2 = 0.64$

Figure 35: Scatterplot and residual plot

process? This question can be investigated using simulation.

If there were no real relationship between height and forearm length, then any of the height values could be paired with any of the forearm values with no loss of information. In the spirit of the comparison of means in the radish experiment, you could then randomly mix up the heights (while leaving the forearm lengths as-is), calculate a new slope, and repeat this process many times to see if the observed slope could be generated simply by randomization. The results of 200 such randomizations are shown in Figure 44. A slope as large as 2.8 is never reached by randomization, which provides strong evidence that the observed slope is not due simply to chance variation. An appropriate conclusion is that there is significant evidence of a linear relationship between forearm length and height.

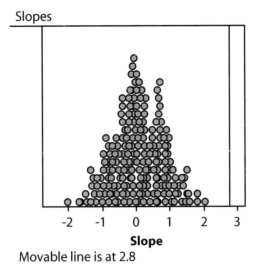

Slopes

Slope
Movable line is at 2.8

Figure 44: Dotplot showing association

Example 1: A Survey of Healthy Lifestyles

A high-school class interested in healthy lifestyles carried out a survey to investigate various questions they thought were related to that issue. A random sample of 50 students selected from those attending a high school on a particular day were asked a variety of health-related questions, including these two:

Do you think you have a healthy lifestyle?

Do you eat breakfast at least three times a week?

The data are given in Table 23.

Table 23: Result of Lifestyle Question

Healthy Lifestyle	Eat Breakfast		
	Yes	No	Total
Yes	19	15	34
No	5	11	16
Total	24	26	50

From these data, collected in a well-designed sample survey, it is possible to estimate the proportion of students in the school who think they have a healthy lifestyle and the proportion who eat breakfast at least three times a week. It also is possible to assess the degree of association between these two categorical variables.

For example, in the lifestyle survey previously described, 24 students in a random sample of 50 students attending a particular high school reported they eat breakfast at least three times per week. Based on this sample survey, it is estimated that the proportion of students at this school who eat breakfast at least three times per week is 24/50 = .48 with a margin of error of:

$$2\sqrt{\frac{(.48)(.52)}{50}} = .14$$

Using the margin of error result from above (.14), the interval of plausible values for the population proportion of students who eat breakfast at least three times a week is (0.34, 0.62). Any population proportion in this interval is consistent with the sample data in the sense that the sample result could reasonably have come from a population having this proportion of students eating breakfast.

To see if the answers to the breakfast and lifestyle questions are associated with each other, you can compare the proportions of *yes* answers to the healthy lifestyle question for those who regularly eat breakfast with those who do not, much like the comparison of means for a randomized experiment. In fact, if a 1 is recorded for each *yes* answer and a 0 for each *no* answer, the sample proportion of *yes* answers is precisely the sample mean. For the observed data, there is a total of 34 1s and 16 0s. Re-randomizing these 50 observations to the groups of size 24 and 26 (corresponding to the yes and no groups on the breakfast question) and calculating the difference in the resulting proportions gave the results in Figure 45. The observed difference in sample proportions (19/24) – (15/26) = 0.21 was matched or exceeded 13 times out of 200 times, for an estimated p-value of 0.065. This is moderately small, so there is some evidence that the difference between the two proprtions might not be a result of chance variation. In other words, the responses to the health lifestyle question and the eating breakfast question appear to be related in the sense that those who think they have a healthy lifestyle also have a tendency to eat breakfast regularly.

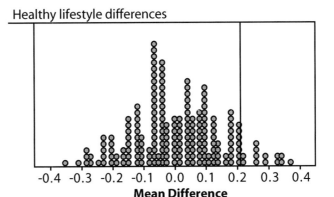

Healthy lifestyle differences

Movable line is at 0.21

Figure 45: Dotplot showing differences in sample proportions

Example 2: An Experimental Investigation of Pulse Rates

On another health-related issue, a student decided to answer the question of whether simply standing for a few minutes increases people's pulses (heart rates) by an appreciable amount. Subjects available for the study were the 15 students in a particular class. The "sit" treatment was randomly assigned to eight of the students; the remaining seven were assigned the "stand" treatment. The measurement recorded was a pulse count for 30 seconds, which was then doubled to approximate a one-minute count. The data, arranged by treatment, are in Table 24. From these data, it is possible to either test the hypothesis that standing does not increase pulse rate, on the average, or to

Table 24: Pulse Data

	Pulse	Group	Category
1	62	1	sit
2	60	1	sit
3	72	1	sit
4	56	1	sit
5	80	1	sit
6	58	1	sit
7	60	1	sit
8	54	1	sit
9	58	2	stand
10	61	2	stand
11	60	2	stand
12	73	2	stand
13	62	2	stand
14	72	2	stand
15	82	2	stand

Table 25: Pulse Data in Matched Pairs

Pulse data: matched pairs

	MPSit	MPStand	Difference
=			
1	68	74	6
2	56	55	-1
3	60	72	12
4	62	64	2
5	56	64	8
6	60	59	-1
7	58	68	10

estimate the difference in mean pulse between those who stand and those who sit. The random assignment to treatments is intended to balance out the unmeasured and uncontrolled variables that could affect the results, such as gender and health conditions. This is called a *completely randomized design.*

However, randomly assigning 15 students to two groups may not be the best way to balance background information that could affect results. It may be better to *block* on a variable related to pulse. Since people have different resting pulse rates, the students in the experiment were blocked by resting pulse rate by pairing the two students with the lowest resting pulse rates, then the two next lowest, and so on. One person in each pair was randomly assigned to sit and the other to stand. The matched pairs data are in Table 25. As in the completely randomized design, the mean difference between sitting and standing pulse rate can be estimated. The main advantage of the blocking is that the variation in the differences (which now form the basis of the analysis) is much less than the variation among the pulse measurements that form the basis of analysis for the completely randomized design.

In the first pulse rate experiment (Table 24), the treatments of "sit" or "stand" were randomly assigned to students. If there is no real difference in pulse rates for these two treatments, then the observed difference in means (4.1 beats per minute) is due to the randomization process itself. To check this out, the data resulting from the experiment can be re-randomized (reassigned to sit or stand after the fact) and a new difference in means recorded. Doing the re-randomization many times will generate a distribution of differences in sample means due to chance alone. Using this distribution, one can assess the likelihood of the original observed difference. Figure 46 shows the results of 200 such re-randomizations. The observed difference of 4.1 was matched or exceeded 48 times, which gives an estimated p-value of 0.24 of seeing a result of 4.1 or greater by chance alone. Because this is a fairly large p-value, it can be concluded that there is little evidence of any real difference in means pulse rates between the sitting and the standing positions based on the observed data.

In the matched pairs design, the randomization occurs within each pair—one person randomly assigned to sit while the other stands. To assess whether the observed difference could be due to chance alone and not due to treatment differences, the re-randomization must occur within the pairs. This implies that the re-randomization is merely a matter of randomly assigning a plus or minus sign to the numerical values of the observed differences. Figure 47 on the follow-

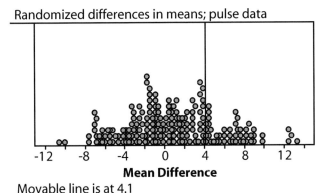

Randomized differences in means; pulse data

Mean Difference

Movable line is at 4.1

Figure 46: Dotplot of randomized differences in means

ing page shows the distribution of the mean differences for 200 such re-randomizations; the observed mean difference of 5.14 was matched or exceeded eight times. Thus, the estimated probability of getting a mean difference of 5.1 or larger by chance alone is 0.04. This very small probability provides evidence that the mean difference can be attributed to something other than chance (induced by the initial randomization process) alone. A better explanation is that standing increases pulse rate, on average, over the sitting rate. The mean difference shows up as significant here, while it did not for the completely randomized design, because the matching reduced the variability. The differences in the matched pairs design have less variability than the individual measurements in the completely randomized design, making it easier to detect a difference in mean pulse for the two treatments.

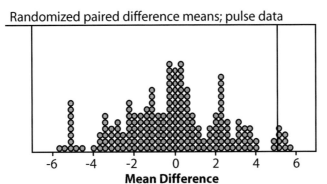

Randomized paired difference means; pulse data

Mean Difference

Movable line is at 5.1

Figure 47: Dotplot of randomized pair difference means

Table 26: U.S. Population (in 1,000s)

Year	Total Persons	Male	Female
1990	249,623	121,714	127,909
1991	252,981	123,416	129,565
1992	256,514	125,247	131,267
1993	259,919	126,971	132,948
1994	263,126	128,597	134,528
1995	266,278	130,215	136,063
1996	269,394	131,807	137,587
1997	272,647	133,474	139,173
1998	275,854	135,130	140,724
1999	279,040	136,803	142,237
2000	282,224	138,470	143,755
2001	285,318	140,076	145,242

Example 3: Observational Study—Rates over Time

Vital statistics are a good example of observational data that are used every day by people in various walks of life. Most of these statistics are reported as rates, so an understanding of rates is a critical skill for high-school graduates. Table 26 shows the U.S. population (in 1,000s) from 1990–2001. Table 27 shows the death rates for sections of the U.S. population over a period of 12 years. Such data recorded over time often are referred to as time series data.

Students' understanding of the rates in Table 27 can be established by posing problems such as:

→ Carefully explain the meaning of the number 1,029.1 in the lower left-hand data cell.

→ Give at least two reasons why the White Male and Black Male entries do not add up to the All Races male entry.

→ Can you tell how many people died in 2001 based on Table 27 alone?

Hopefully, students will quickly realize that they cannot change from rates of death to frequencies of death without knowledge of the population sizes. Table 26 provides the population sizes overall, as well as for the male and female categories.

Noting that the population figures are in thousands but the rates are per 100,000, it takes a little thinking

Table 27: U.S. Death Rates (Deaths per 100,000 of Population)

Year	All Races		White		Black	
	Male	Female	Male	Female	Male	Female
1990	1202.8	750.9	1165.9	728.8	1644.5	975.1
1991	1180.5	738.2	1143.1	716.1	1626.1	963.3
1992	1158.3	725.5	1122.4	704.1	1587.8	942.5
1993	1177.3	745.9	1138.9	724.1	1632.2	969.5
1994	1155.5	738.6	1118.7	717.5	1592.8	954.6
1995	1143.9	739.4	1107.5	718.7	1585.7	955.9
1996	1115.7	733.0	1082.9	713.6	1524.2	940.3
1997	1088.1	725.6	1059.1	707.8	1458.8	922.1
1998	1069.4	724.7	1042.0	707.3	1430.5	921.6
1999	1067.0	734.0	1040.0	716.6	1432.6	933.6
2000	1053.8	731.4	1029.4	715.3	1403.5	927.6
2001	1029.1	721.8	1006.1	706.7	1375.0	912.5

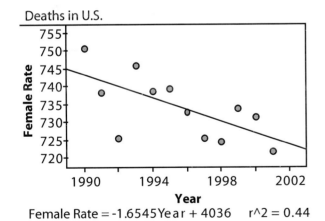

Female Rate = -1.6545Year + 4036   r^2 = 0.44

Figure 48: Scatterplot of death rates

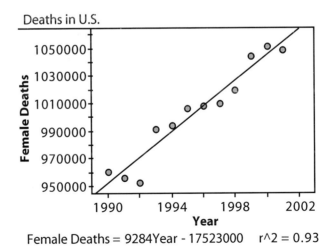

Female Deaths = 9284Year - 17523000   r^2 = 0.93

Figure 49: Scatterplot of actual deaths

on a student's part to go from rates to counts by making the computation shown in the formula:

Female Deaths

$$= \text{Female Death Rate} \cdot \left(\frac{\text{Female Population}}{100} \right)$$

Some time series questions can now be explored. For example, how does the pattern of female death rates over time compare to the pattern of actual female deaths? The plots of Figures 48 and 49 provide a visual impression. The death rates are trending downward over time, with considerable variation, but the actual deaths are going up.

Students will discover that the picture for males is quite different, which can lead to interesting discussions.

Example 4: Graphs: Distortions of Reality?

Study the graph pictured in Figure 50. Do you see any weaknesses in this graphic presentation? If so, describe them and explain how they could be corrected.

Here are some plausible plots to correct errors of interpretation, and to raise other questions. Better presentations begin with a data table, such as Table 28, and then proceed to more standard graphical displays of such data.

The plot in Figure 51 shows total and African-American enrollments on the same scale. When viewed this

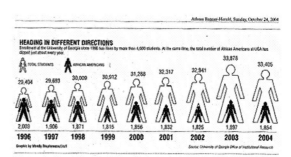

Figure 50: Distorted graph [source: *Athens Banner-Herald*]

Table 28: Enrollment Data

Year	Total Students	African Americans
1996	29404	2003
1997	29693	1906
1998	30009	1871
1999	30912	1815
2000	31288	1856
2001	32317	1832
2002	32941	1825
2003	33878	1897
2004	33405	1845

way, one can see that the latter is a small part of the former, with little change, by comparison, over the years.

By viewing African-American enrollments by themselves, one can see that the marked decrease between 1996 and 2002 may be turning around—or leveling off.

However, the ratio of African American to total enrollment is still on the decrease!

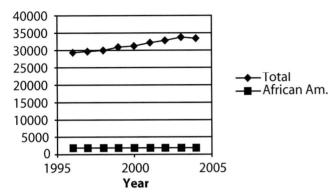

Figure 51: Plot of African-American vs. total enrollments

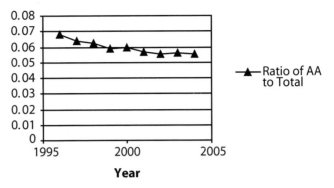

Figure 53: Ratio of African-American to total enrollments

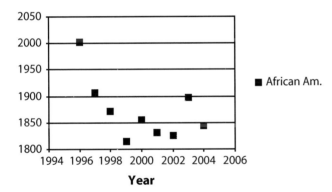

Figure 52: Plot of African-American enrollments only

References

Cobb, G. and Moore, D. (2000). "Statistics and Mathematics: Tension and Cooperation," *American Mathematical Monthly*, pp. 615-630.

College Board (2006). *College Board Standards for College Success™: Mathematics and Statistics.*

College Entrance Examination Board (2004). *Course Description: Statistics.* New York: College Board.

Conference Board of the Mathematical Sciences (2001). *The Mathematical Education of Teachers.* Providence, RI, and Washington, DC: American Mathematical Society and Mathematical Association of America.

Conover, W. J. (1999). *Practical Nonparametric Statistics.* John Wiley and Sons, Page 235 (Equation 17).

Consumer Reports (June 1993) Hot dogs. 51(6), 364-367.

Data-Driven Mathematics Series (1998), New York: Pearson Learning (Dale Seymour Publications).

Gnanadesikan, Mrudulla, Richard L. Scheaffer, James M. Landwehr, Ann E. Watkins, Peter Barbella, James Kepner, Claire M. Newman, Thomas E. Obremski, and Jim Swift (1995). *Quantitative Literacy Series,* New York: Pearson Learning (Dale Seymour Publications).

Hollander, Miles and Proschan, Frank (1984). *The Statistical Exorcist: Dispelling Statistics Anxiety.* Marcel Dekker, Pages 83–88 and 121–130.

Holmes, Peter (2001). "Correlation: From Picture to Formula," *Teaching Statistics*, 23(3):67–70.

Kader, Gary (1999). "Means and MADS," *Mathematics Teaching in the Middle School*, 4(6):398–403.

Kader, Gary and Perry, Mike (1984). "Learning Statistics with Technology," *Mathematics Teaching in the Middle School*, 1(2):130–136.

Moore, D. and Cobb, G. (1997). "Mathematics, Statistics, and Teaching," *American Mathematical Monthly*, 104, 801–823.

National Assessment Governing Board (2004). *Mathematics Framework for 2005 National Assessment of Educational Progress.* Available: *www.amstat.org/education/gaise/4.*

National Council of Teachers of Mathematics (1989). *Curriculum and Evaluation Standards for School Mathematics.* Reston, VA: The Council.

National Council of Teachers of Mathematics (2002–2004). *Navigating through Data Analysis and Probability Series.* Reston, VA: The Council.

National Council of Teachers of Mathematics (2000). *Principles and Standards for School Mathematics.* Reston, VA: The Council.

Steen, Lynn, ed. (2001). *Mathematics and Democracy: The Case for Quantitative Literacy.* National Council on Education and the Disciplines. Princeton: Woodrow Wilson Foundation.

U.S. Census Bureau. (2005). *Statistical Abstract of the United States 2004–2005*, Table No. 70. Live Births, Deaths, Marriages, and Divorces: 1950 to 2002.

Utts, Jessica A. (1999). *Seeing Through Statistics.* Pacific Grove, CA: Duxbury, 2nd ed.